It's another great book from CGP...

GCSE Core Science is all about **understanding how science works**.
And not only that — understanding it well enough to be able to **question**
what you hear on TV and read in the papers.

But don't panic. This book includes all the **science facts** you need to learn,
and shows you how they work in the real world. It even includes
a **free** Online Edition you can read on your computer or tablet.

How to get your free Online Edition

Just go to **cgpbooks.co.uk/extras** and enter this code...

3505 5107 0268 4421

By the way, this code only works for one person. If somebody else has used
this book before you, they might have already claimed the Online Edition.

CGP — still the best! ☺

Our sole aim here at CGP is to produce the highest
quality books — carefully written, immaculately presented
and dangerously close to being funny.

Then we work our socks off to get them
out to you — at the cheapest possible prices.

Contents

MODULE B2 — UNDERSTANDING OUR ENVIRONMENT

MODULE C2 — CHEMICAL RESOURCES

MODULE P2 — LIVING FOR THE FUTURE

Published by CGP

From original material by Richard Parsons.

Editors:
Luke Antieul, Katie Braid, Emma Elder, David Hickinson, Edmund Robinson, Helen Ronan,
Lyn Setchell, Hayley Thompson, Jane Towle, Dawn Wright.

Contributors:
Mike Bossart

ISBN: 978 1 84146 710 8

With thanks to Chris Elliss, James Foster, Ian Francis, Helena Hayes, Judith Hayes,
Edmund Robinson, Jamie Sinclair and Sarah Williams for the proofreading.

With thanks to Jan Greenway, Laura Jakubowski and Laura Stoney for the copyright research.

Photo of Kwashiorkor sufferer on page 12 courtesy of Tom D Thacher, MD.

With thanks to Science Photo Library for permission to use the image on page 51.

With thanks to iStockphoto.com for permission to use the image on page 100.

Page 114 contains public sector information published by the Health and Safety Executive and
licensed under the Open Government Licence v1.0.

GORE-TEX®, GORE®, and designs are registered trademarks of W L Gore & Associates.
This book contains copyrighted material reproduced with the permission of
W.L. Gore and Associates. Copyright 2011 W.L. Gore & Associates.

Every effort has been made to locate copyright holders and obtain permission to reproduce
sources. For those sources where it has been difficult to trace the originator of the work,
we would be grateful for information. If any copyright holder would like us to make an
amendment to the acknowledgements, please notify us and we will gladly update the book at
the next reprint. Thank you.

www.cgpbooks.co.uk

Printed by Elanders Ltd, Newcastle upon Tyne.
Clipart from Corel®

The Scientific Process

For your <u>exams</u> and your <u>controlled assessment</u> you need to know about how the <u>world of science</u> works.

Science is All About Testing a Hypothesis

'Controlled assessment' is the scary name for the piece of coursework you have to do. See page 8 for more.

Scientists make an observation

1) Scientists <u>observe</u> (look at) something they don't understand — e.g. an illness that a person has.
2) Then they come up with a possible <u>explanation</u> for what they've observed.
3) This explanation is called a <u>hypothesis</u>.

Hundreds of years ago, we thought demons caused illness.

They test their hypothesis

1) Next, they <u>test</u> whether the hypothesis might be <u>right or not</u>.
2) They begin by making a <u>prediction</u> — a statement based on the hypothesis that can be <u>tested</u> by carrying out <u>experiments</u>.
3) Then they <u>collect evidence</u> (<u>data</u> from <u>experiments</u>) to test their prediction.
4) If their prediction is <u>right</u>, this shows that their <u>hypothesis might be right too</u>.
5) This <u>doesn't</u> mean the hypothesis is <u>true</u> though — other predictions might turn out to be <u>wrong</u>.

Then we thought it was caused by 'bad blood' (and treated it with leeches).

Other scientists test the hypothesis too

1) Once a scientist has come up with and tested a hypothesis, they'll show their work to <u>other scientists</u> to be <u>checked</u>. This is called the <u>peer review</u> process.
2) They then show their work to everyone by printing it in <u>journals</u> (science magazines) and talking about it at <u>conferences</u> (meetings).
3) Other scientists then try to <u>repeat</u> the results of the original experiment. They also carry out their own experiments to <u>collect more evidence</u>.

Now we know most illnesses are due to microorganisms.

The hypothesis is accepted or changed

1) If all the experiments back up the hypothesis, scientists start to have a lot of <u>trust</u> in it.
2) But, if someone does an experiment and the results <u>don't</u> fit with the hypothesis then scientists must:
   a) <u>change</u> the hypothesis, OR
   b) come up with a completely <u>new</u> hypothesis.

You expect me to believe that — then show me the evidence...

If scientists think something is true, they need to find evidence to convince others. This is all part of <u>testing a hypothesis</u>. The hypothesis might survive these tests, but it might not. It's how science moves on.

Scientific Information and Development

In everyday life (and in your <u>exams</u> unfortunately) you'll come across lots of <u>scientific information</u>.

Scientific Ideas Change as New Evidence is Found

1) Scientific explanations are <u>provisional</u> — they only explain the evidence that's <u>currently available</u>.
2) New evidence may come up that <u>can't be explained</u>.
3) Scientific explanations are <u>more convincing</u> when there's a <u>lot of evidence</u> to support them.
4) But scientific explanations <u>never</u> become <u>fact</u>. As <u>new evidence</u> is found, hypotheses can <u>change</u> or be <u>replaced</u>.

Different Scientists Can Have Different Explanations

1) Different scientists might come up with <u>different explanations</u> for the <u>same evidence</u>.
2) More <u>predictions</u> and <u>experiments</u> would help to work out which explanation is the most <u>convincing</u>.
3) You might be given some <u>scientific evidence</u> and some <u>explanations</u>.
   You need to be able to say whether the evidence does or doesn't <u>support</u> the explanations.
4) This is easy — just look to see whether it's a <u>sensible explanation</u> to make from the evidence, or whether the explanation <u>just doesn't fit</u> with the evidence at all.

Scientific Information Can't Always be Trusted

1) When you're given some scientific information, <u>don't</u> just <u>believe it straight away</u>.
2) You need to think about whether there's any <u>evidence to support it</u>.

- Someone might give scientific information <u>without any evidence</u> to back it up.
- This might be because there's <u>no evidence</u> to support what they're saying.
- Information that isn't backed up with any <u>evidence</u> could just be an <u>opinion</u> — you've got <u>no way</u> of telling whether it's <u>true or not</u>.

Society Affects the Development of Science

1) The question of whether we should or shouldn't use new scientific developments <u>can't be answered</u> by <u>experiments</u> — there is <u>no "right" or "wrong" answer</u>.
2) The best we can do is get a <u>consensus</u> from society — a <u>decision</u> that <u>most people</u> are more or less happy to live by.
3) <u>Science</u> can give <u>more information</u> to help people make this decision, and the decision might <u>change</u> over time. But in the end it's up to <u>people</u> and their <u>sense of right and wrong</u>.
4) <u>Decisions</u> about how science is <u>used</u> can also be affected by lots of <u>other factors</u>, e.g. <u>economic</u>, <u>social</u> and <u>cultural</u> issues.

It's a scientific fact that the Moon's made of cheese...

Whenever you're given any scientific information just stop for a second. Ask yourself how <u>convincing</u> it really is — look to see if any <u>evidence</u> has been used to support it. It might just be an <u>opinion</u> — there's a big difference.

Planning Investigations

Here's how <u>practical investigations</u> should be carried out — by both <u>professional scientists</u> and <u>you</u>.

To Make an Investigation a Fair Test You Have to Control the Variables

Investigations that you plan should always be a <u>fair test</u>.

1) In a lab experiment you usually <u>change one thing</u> (a variable) and <u>measure</u> how it affects <u>another thing</u> (another variable).

> **EXAMPLE:** you might change only the temperature of an enzyme-controlled reaction and measure how it affects the rate of reaction.

2) <u>Everything else</u> that could affect the results needs to <u>stay the same</u>.
Then you know that the thing you're <u>changing</u> is the <u>only</u> thing that's affecting the results.

> **EXAMPLE** continued: you need to keep the pH the same. If you don't, you won't know if any change in the rate of reaction is caused by the change in temperature, or the change in pH.

3) The variable that you <u>change</u> is called the <u>independent</u> variable.

4) The variable that's <u>measured</u> is called the <u>dependent</u> variable.

5) The variables that you <u>keep the same</u> are called <u>control</u> variables.

> **EXAMPLE** continued:
> Independent = temperature
> Dependent = rate of reaction
> Control = pH

The Equipment Used has to be Right for the Job

1) You need to make sure you choose the <u>right equipment</u>.

2) For example, the measuring equipment you use has to be able to <u>accurately</u> measure the chemicals you're using. If you need to measure out 11 ml of a liquid, use a measuring cylinder that can measure to 1 ml, not 5 or 10 ml.

3) The <u>smallest change</u> a measuring instrument can <u>measure</u> is called its RESOLUTION.
E.g. some mass balances have a resolution of 1 g and some have a resolution of 0.1 g.

4) You should also be able to <u>explain why</u> you've chosen each bit of kit.

> Accurate measurements are really close to the true value of what you're measuring.

Experiments Must be Safe

1) There are lots of <u>hazards</u> (dangers) you could be faced with during an investigation, e.g. <u>radiation</u>, <u>electricity</u>, <u>gas</u>, <u>chemicals</u> and <u>fire</u>.

2) You should always make sure that you think of <u>all</u> the hazards there might be.

3) You should also come up with ways of <u>reducing the risks</u> from the hazards you've spotted.

4) For example, for an experiment involving a <u>Bunsen burner</u>: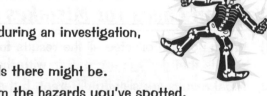

> Hazard:
> • Bunsen burner is a fire risk.
> Ways risk can be reduced:
> • Keep chemicals that can catch fire away from the Bunsen.
> • Never leave the Bunsen alone when lit.
> • Always turn on the yellow safety flame when not in use.

Hazard: revision boredom. Reduce by: using CGP books

Wow, all this even before you've started the investigation — it really does make them run more smoothly though.

Getting the Data Right

You'll want to make sure that you get the best results you possibly can. Here's a few things you can do:

Trial Runs Help Figure out the Range and Interval of Variable Values

1) A trial run is a quick version of your experiment.

2) Trial runs help you work out whether your plan is right or not — you might decide to make some changes after trying out your method.

3) They're used to figure out the range of independent variable values used (the highest and lowest value).

4) And they're used to figure out the interval (gaps) between the values too.

> Enzyme-controlled reaction example from previous page continued:
> - You might do trial runs at 10, 20, 30, 40 and 50 °C. If there was no reaction at 10 or 50 °C, you might narrow the range to 20-40 °C.
> - If using 10 °C intervals gives you a big change in rate of reaction you might decide to use 5 °C intervals, e.g. 20, 25, 30, 35 °C...

Data Should be as Reliable and Accurate as Possible

1) Reliable results are results that always come out the same every time you do the same experiment.

2) If your results are reliable they're more likely to be true. This means you can have more trust in your conclusions.

3) You can make your results more reliable by repeating the readings at least twice (so that you have at least three readings). Then you can calculate the mean (average, see next page).

4) Checking your results match with secondary sources, e.g. studies that other people have done, also makes your data more reliable.

5) You should also always make sure that your results are accurate.

6) Really accurate results are those that are really close to the true answer.

7) You can get accurate results by making sure the equipment you're using is sensitive enough (see previous page).

You Can Check For Mistakes Made When Collecting Data

1) When you've collected all the results for an experiment, you should have a look to see if there are any results that don't seem to fit in with the rest.

2) Most results are slightly different, but any that are totally different are called anomalous results.

3) They're caused by human errors, e.g. by a whoopsie when measuring.

4) The only way to stop them happening is by taking all your measurements as carefully as possible.

5) If you ever get any anomalous results, you should try to work out what happened.

6) If you can work out what happened (e.g. you measured something wrong) you can ignore them when processing your results.

Reliable data — it won't ever forget your birthday...

All this stuff is really important — your data will be meaningless if it's not reliable and accurate. So give this page a read through a couple of times and your data will be the envy of all the scientists in the world. Yes, all of them.

Processing, Presenting and Interpreting Data

The fun doesn't stop once you've collected your data — it then needs to be **processed** and **presented**...

Data Needs to be Organised

1) Data that's been collected needs to be <u>organised</u> so it can be processed later on.

2) <u>Tables</u> are dead useful for <u>organising data</u>.

3) You should always make sure that <u>each column</u> has a <u>heading</u> and that you've included the <u>units</u>.

Test tube	Result (ml)	Repeat 1 (ml)	Repeat 2 (ml)
A	28	37	32
B	47	51	60
C	68	72	70

Data Can be Processed Using a Bit of Maths

1) <u>Raw data</u> just isn't that useful. To make it useful, you have to <u>process</u> it in some way.

2) One of the most simple calculations you can do is the <u>mean</u> (average):

> To calculate the <u>mean</u> **ADD TOGETHER** all the data values. Then **DIVIDE** by the total number of values. You usually do this to get a single value from several <u>repeats</u> of your experiment.

Test tube	Result (ml)	Repeat 1 (ml)	Repeat 2 (ml)	Mean (ml)
A	28	37	32	(28 + 37 + 32) ÷ 3 = 32.3
B	47	51	60	(47 + 51 + 60) ÷ 3 = 52.7
C	68	72	70	(68 + 72 + 70) ÷ 3 = 70.0

Different Types of Data Should be Presented in Different Ways

1) You need to <u>present</u> your data so that it's easier to see any <u>patterns</u>.

2) Different types of investigations give you <u>different types</u> of data, so you'll always have to <u>choose</u> what the best way to present your data is.

Pie charts can be used to present the same sort of data as bar charts. They're mostly used when the data is in percentages or fractions.

Bar Charts

1) If the independent variable comes in <u>clear categories</u> (e.g. blood types, metals) you should use a <u>bar chart</u> to display the data.

2) You also use them if the independent variable can be counted in <u>chunks</u>, where there are no in-between values. For example, number of people (because you can't have half a person).

3) There are some <u>golden rules</u> you need to follow for <u>drawing</u> bar charts:

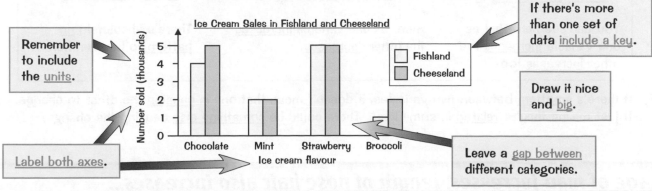

Remember to include the <u>units</u>.

If there's more than one set of data <u>include a key</u>.

Draw it nice and <u>big</u>.

<u>Label both axes</u>.

Leave a <u>gap between</u> different categories.

Ice Cream Sales in Fishland and Cheeseland

Number sold (thousands) — Ice cream flavour: Chocolate, Mint, Strawberry, Broccoli

Fishland / Cheeseland

Processing, Presenting and Interpreting Data

Line Graphs

If the independent variable can have <u>any value</u> within a <u>range</u>, (e.g. length, volume, temperature) you should use a <u>line graph</u> to display the data.

Remember to include the <u>units</u>.

The <u>dependent</u> variable (the thing you measure) goes on the <u>y-axis</u> (the <u>vertical</u> one).

The <u>independent</u> variable (the thing you change) goes on the <u>x-axis</u> (the <u>horizontal</u> one).

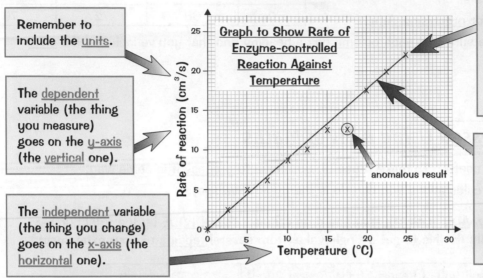

Graph to Show Rate of Enzyme-controlled Reaction Against Temperature

Rate of reaction (cm³/s)

Temperature (°C)

anomalous result

When plotting points, use a <u>sharp pencil</u> and make a <u>neat little cross</u> (don't do blobs).

nice clear mark

smudged unclear marks

<u>Don't join the dots up</u>. You should draw a <u>line of best fit</u> (or a <u>curve of best fit</u>). Try to draw the line <u>through</u> or as <u>near</u> to <u>as many points as possible</u>, ignoring anomalous results.

You can use line graphs to <u>process</u> data a bit more.
For example, if 'time' is on the x-axis, you can calculate the <u>gradient</u> (<u>slope</u>) of the line to find the <u>rate of reaction</u>:

1) Gradient = y ÷ x

2) You can calculate the gradient of the <u>whole line</u> or a <u>section</u> of it.

3) The rate would be in <u>cm³/s</u> (cubic centimetres of gas per second).

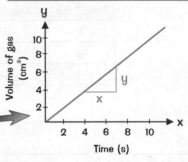

Volume of gas (cm³)

Time (s)

Line Graphs Can Show Patterns in Data

1) When you're carrying out an investigation it's not enough to just present your data — you've also got to find any <u>patterns</u> in the data.

2) Line graphs are great for showing patterns in data.

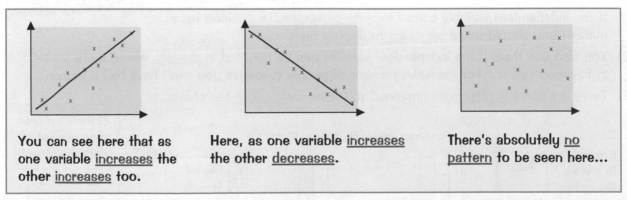

You can see here that as one variable <u>increases</u> the other <u>increases</u> too.

Here, as one variable <u>increases</u> the other <u>decreases</u>.

There's absolutely <u>no</u> <u>pattern</u> to be seen here...

3) If there's a <u>pattern</u> between two variables, it doesn't mean that one is <u>causing</u> the other to change. It just means they're <u>related</u> in some way. There could be <u>something else</u> causing the change.

As age of man increases, length of nose hair also increases...

<u>Process</u>, <u>present</u>, <u>interpret</u>... data's like a difficult child — it needs a lot of attention. Go on, make it happy.

Concluding and Evaluating

At the end of an investigation, the <u>conclusion</u> and <u>evaluation</u> are waiting. Don't worry, they won't bite.

A Conclusion is a Summary of What You've Learnt

1) Once you've collected, presented and analysed your data, you need to come to a <u>conclusion</u>.

2) You just have to <u>look at your data</u> and <u>say what pattern you see</u>.

EXAMPLE: The table on the right shows the heights of pea plant seedlings grown for three weeks with different fertilisers.

Fertiliser	Mean growth (mm)
A	13.5
B	19.5
No fertiliser	5.5

CONCLUSION: Fertiliser <u>B</u> makes <u>pea plant</u> seedlings grow taller over a <u>three week</u> period than fertiliser A.

3) You also need to use the data that's been <u>collected</u> to <u>justify</u> the conclusion (back it up).

EXAMPLE continued: Fertiliser B made the pea plants grow 6 mm more on average than fertiliser A.

4) It's important that the conclusion <u>matches the data</u> it's based on — it <u>shouldn't say anything that the data doesn't show</u>.

EXAMPLE continued: You can't conclude that fertiliser B makes <u>any other type of plant</u> grow taller than fertiliser A — the results could be totally different.

5) You should also use your own <u>scientific knowledge</u> (the stuff you've learnt in class) to try to <u>explain</u> the conclusion.

Evaluation — Describe How it Could be Improved

In an evaluation you look back over the whole investigation.

I'd value this E somewhere in the region of 250-300k

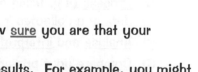

1) You should comment on the <u>method</u> — was the <u>equipment suitable</u>? Was it a <u>fair test</u>?

2) Comment on the <u>quality</u> of the <u>results</u> — were they <u>reliable</u> and <u>accurate</u>?

3) Were there any <u>anomalous results</u> — if there were <u>none</u> then <u>say so</u>.

4) If there were any anomalous results, try to <u>explain</u> them — were they caused by <u>errors</u> in measurement? Were there any other <u>variables</u> that could have <u>affected</u> the results?

5) When you look back at your investigation like this, you'll be able to say how <u>sure</u> you are that your conclusion is <u>right</u>.

6) Then you can suggest any <u>changes</u> that would <u>improve</u> the quality of the results. For example, you might suggest changing the way you controlled a variable, or changing the interval of values you measured.

7) This would mean you could be <u>more sure</u> about your conclusion.

8) When you suggest an improvement to the investigation, always say <u>why</u> you think this would make the results <u>better</u>.

Evaluation — in my next study I will make sure I don't burn the lab down...

I know it doesn't seem very nice, but writing about where you went <u>wrong</u> is an important skill. It shows you've got a really good understanding of what the investigation was <u>about</u>. It's difficult for me — I'm always right.

Controlled Assessment

You'll probably carry out a few investigations as you go through the course. But at some point you'll have to do the one that counts... the <u>controlled assessment</u>. Here's a bit about it...

There are Three Parts to the Controlled Assessment

① Research and Collecting Secondary Data

For Part 1 you'll be given some material to introduce the task and a <u>research question</u>. You need to:

1) <u>Carry out research</u> and collect <u>secondary data</u> (data that other people have collected).
2) Show that you thought about all the <u>different sources</u> you could have used (e.g. books, the Internet) and <u>chose</u> the <u>best ones</u>. You also need to explain <u>why</u> you chose those sources.
3) Write a <u>full list</u> (bibliography) of all the sources you used.
4) <u>Present</u> all the data you collected in the <u>best</u> way, e.g. using tables.

② Planning and Collecting Primary Data

For Part 2 you'll be given a <u>hypothesis</u> (see p. 1) to test and some more material to read. You need to:

1) <u>Plan</u> an experiment to test the hypothesis you've been given. Think about:
   * What <u>equipment</u> you're going to use (and <u>why</u> that equipment is <u>right for the job</u>).
   * What <u>measurements</u> you're going to take of the <u>dependent variable</u>.
   * How you're going to make sure your results are <u>accurate</u> and <u>reliable</u>.
   * What <u>range</u> of values and <u>interval</u> you will use for the <u>independent variable</u>.
   * What variables you're going to <u>control</u> (and <u>how</u> you're going to do it).
   * How many times you're going to <u>repeat</u> the experiment.
2) Say what the <u>risks</u> of the experiment will be and how you'll <u>reduce</u> them.
3) <u>Carry out</u> the experiment to collect <u>primary data</u>.
4) <u>Present</u> all the data you collected in the <u>best</u> way, e.g. using tables.

Don't forget to <u>explain</u> all the choices you made when planning the experiment.

③ Analysis and Evaluation

For Part 3 you'll have to complete a <u>question paper</u>. It'll ask you to do things like:

1) <u>Process</u> (e.g. using a bit of maths) and <u>present</u> (e.g. using graphs) <u>both</u> the primary and secondary data you collected in Part 1 and Part 2.
2) <u>Analyse</u> and <u>interpret</u> the data to find any <u>patterns</u>.
3) <u>Compare</u> your primary and secondary data to look for <u>similarities and differences</u>.
4) Write a <u>conclusion</u> based on your primary data.
   Make sure you back it up with your own <u>scientific knowledge</u>.
5) Say whether the <u>secondary data</u> you collected <u>supports</u> the conclusion.
6) <u>Evaluate</u> the <u>methods</u> you used to collect the data and the <u>quality of the data</u> that was collected.
7) Say how <u>sure</u> you are about your <u>conclusion</u>.
8) Make <u>suggestions</u> for how the investigation could be <u>improved</u>. You'll also need to say <u>why</u> your suggestions would be an improvement.

Read this through and your assessment will be well under control...

You could use this page like a tick list for the controlled assessment — to make sure you don't forget anything.

Fitness and Blood Pressure

Ahh. Fitness and blood pressure. Just the stuff to get your <u>blood pumping</u> and your brain in gear.

Being Fit is Not the Same as Being Healthy

You need to know the difference between being <u>fit</u> and being <u>healthy</u>...

- Being <u>HEALTHY</u> means being <u>free from disease</u>.
- Being <u>FIT</u> is a measure of <u>how well</u> you can perform <u>physical tasks</u>.

There are Different Ways to Measure Fitness

You can <u>measure</u> someone's fitness by measuring their:

1) STRENGTH — e.g. how well they can <u>lift weights</u>.
2) SPEED — e.g. how <u>fast</u> they can <u>run</u>.
3) AGILITY — e.g. how well they can <u>climb</u> a tree.
4) FLEXIBILITY — e.g. how <u>easily</u> they can do the <u>splits</u>.
5) STAMINA — e.g. how <u>long</u> they can <u>keep running</u> for.

Stamina is a good indication of <u>CARDIOVASCULAR EFFICIENCY</u>.
This is the ability of the <u>heart</u> to <u>supply</u> the <u>muscles</u> with <u>oxygen</u>.

Blood is Pumped Around Your Body Under Pressure

1) The blood is <u>pumped</u> around the body by <u>contractions</u> of the <u>heart</u> muscles.
2) These contractions <u>increase</u> the <u>pressure</u> of the blood so that it can reach <u>every part</u> of the body.
3) The blood leaves the heart and flows through <u>arteries</u>. It flows back to the heart through <u>veins</u>.
4) The blood pressure is at its <u>highest</u> when the heart <u>contracts</u> — this is called the <u>systolic pressure</u>.
5) When the heart <u>relaxes</u>, the pressure is at its <u>lowest</u> — this is called the <u>diastolic pressure</u>.
6) Blood pressure is measured in <u>mm of mercury</u> (<u>mmHg</u>).
7) There are some things that can <u>increase</u> your <u>blood pressure</u>.
   These include:

- <u>smoking</u>
- being <u>overweight</u>
- drinking too much <u>alcohol</u>
- being under lots of <u>stress</u>

8) High blood pressure can be <u>decreased</u> by doing regular
   <u>exercise</u> and eating a <u>balanced diet</u>.

My old P.E. teacher was really fit...

The factors mentioned above only <u>increase the chance</u> of someone developing high blood pressure. None of them will <u>definitely</u> give them it. So someone who is overweight and drinks too much alcohol <u>might</u> have perfectly healthy blood pressure. But they'd be <u>less likely</u> to suffer <u>problems</u> if they <u>lost weight</u> and drank <u>less alcohol</u>.

High Blood Pressure and Heart Disease

Smoking, in case you hadn't realised by now, is really quite BAD for you. And so is eating a lot of foods high in salt and fat. They can all give you high blood pressure, which can lead to heart disease.

Smoking Can Increase Blood Pressure and Lead to Heart Disease

1) Cigarette smoke contains lots of nasty chemicals — some of which can increase blood pressure:

CARBON MONOXIDE — this reduces how much oxygen the blood can carry. To make up for this heart rate increases. The heart contracts more often, which increases blood pressure.

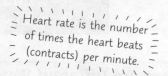
Heart rate is the number of times the heart beats (contracts) per minute.

NICOTINE — this increases heart rate. The heart contracts more often, increasing blood pressure.

2) High blood pressure and smoking can both lead to heart disease.

3) Heart disease is any disease that affects the heart. This includes things like heart attacks.

A Poor Diet Can Also Lead to Heart Disease

If your diet is high in saturated fat or salt, you may be more at risk of getting heart disease.

Saturated Fats Can Cause a Build Up of Cholesterol

1) Cholesterol is a fatty substance.

2) Eating lots of saturated fat has been linked to high levels of cholesterol in the blood.

3) You need some cholesterol. But if you get too much cholesterol it starts to build up in your arteries (a type of blood vessel — see previous page).

4) This forms plaques (lumps) in the artery wall, which narrow the arteries.

5) The plaques reduce the flow of blood, which can lead to a heart attack.

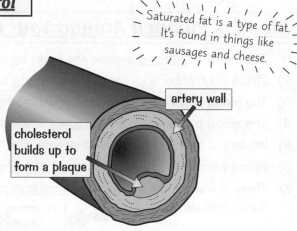
Saturated fat is a type of fat. It's found in things like sausages and cheese.

artery wall

cholesterol builds up to form a plaque

High Salt Levels Can Increase Blood Pressure

1) You need salt as part of a healthy diet. But eating too much salt can cause high blood pressure.

2) High blood pressure increases the risk of damage to the arteries.

3) This damage can trigger the build up of plaques, which can lead to a heart attack.

Don't let Exam stress send your blood pressure through the roof...

The number of people getting heart disease in the UK is going up. You might be given some data on this in the exam and asked to analyse it — but don't panic if you do. Just remember that heart disease is linked to stuff like the amount of saturated fat you eat and the build up of cholesterol plaques.

Eating Healthily

You need a <u>balanced diet</u> to give you energy and make sure that everything keeps working properly.

A Balanced Diet Keeps You Healthy

1) Your <u>diet</u> is the food you eat. A <u>balanced diet</u> contains all the <u>nutrients</u> you need to stay healthy:

NUTRIENTS	FUNCTIONS
Carbohydrates	Provide energy.
Fats	Provide energy.
Proteins	Needed for growth and repair of tissue, and to provide energy in emergencies.
Vitamins	Many functions: e.g. vitamin C is needed to prevent scurvy.
Minerals	Many functions: e.g. iron is needed to make haemoglobin for healthy blood.
Water	To prevent dehydration (where the body doesn't have enough water).

2) As well as the nutrients in the table, you also need <u>fibre</u> to <u>prevent constipation</u> (difficulty pooing).

3) Nutrients are made up of different things. You need to know that:

- <u>Carbohydrates</u> are made up of <u>simple sugars</u> like <u>glucose</u>.
- <u>Fats</u> are made up of <u>fatty acids</u> and <u>glycerol</u>.
- <u>Proteins</u> are made up of <u>amino acids</u>.

A Balanced Diet is Different for Different People

A balanced diet <u>isn't</u> a set thing — it's <u>different</u> for everyone.
The balance of different nutrients a person needs depends on things like:

Age ➜ <u>Children</u> and <u>teenagers</u> need more <u>protein</u> for <u>growth</u>.

Gender ➜ <u>Females</u> need more <u>iron</u> to replace the iron <u>lost</u> in <u>blood</u> during their <u>period</u>.

Physical activity ➜ <u>Active people</u> need more <u>carbohydrates</u> for <u>energy</u>.

Some People Choose to Eat a Different Diet

Some people <u>choose</u> not to eat some foods for all sorts of reasons:

1) <u>Religious</u> reasons — e.g. <u>Hindus</u> don't eat cows because they believe they're <u>sacred</u>.

2) <u>Personal</u> reasons — <u>vegetarians</u> don't eat meat for various reasons — some think it's <u>cruel</u> to animals, some don't like the <u>taste</u> and some think it's <u>healthier</u>. <u>Vegans</u> don't eat any products from animals, e.g. milk, eggs and cheese.

3) <u>Medical</u> reasons — some people are <u>allergic</u> to foods (e.g. nuts).
They get a <u>severe reaction</u> which can sometimes <u>kill</u> them.

I think the problem is that I've got an allergy to sprouts...

The examiners might throw you a question where you've got to interpret <u>data</u> on diet. But so long as you've learned all the stuff on this page about the <u>different nutrients</u> and why people have different <u>balanced diets</u> it'll be dead easy.

Diet Problems

You are what you eat, apparently. That makes me baked beans. But at least I'm not toast.

Eating Too Little Can Cause Problems

1) Eating <u>too little protein</u> can cause a condition called <u>kwashiorkor</u>. A common symptom is a <u>swollen stomach</u>.

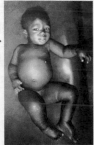

A kwashiorkor sufferer

Photo courtesy of Tom D. Thacher, MD.

2) In <u>developing</u> (poorer) <u>countries</u> lots of people have diets that are <u>too low in protein</u>. There are two main reasons for this:
   - <u>Overpopulation</u> means there's too many people and not enough <u>protein-rich food</u> for everyone.
   - There isn't a lot of <u>money</u> to spend on <u>agriculture</u> (farming) — so it's difficult to produce <u>enough protein-rich food</u> for everyone.

3) The <u>amount of protein</u> you need to eat <u>each day</u> is called your <u>Estimated Average daily Requirement</u> (EAR). You can <u>calculate</u> your EAR using this formula:

$$\text{EAR (in g)} = 0.6 \times \text{body mass (in kg)}$$

Body mass is just how much you weigh — don't forget it should be in kilograms.

4) Some <u>eating disorders</u> (e.g. anorexia) can also result in a <u>poor diet</u>.

5) These disorders are usually caused by <u>low self-esteem</u> and a <u>desire to be 'perfect'</u> — sufferers have a <u>poor self-image</u>.

6) A <u>poor diet</u> can cause loads of <u>other illnesses</u>, e.g. liver failure, kidney failure and heart attacks. They can even result in <u>death</u>.

Eating Too Much Can Lead to Obesity

1) <u>Obesity</u> means being <u>20%</u> (or more) <u>over recommended body weight</u>.

2) The main causes of obesity are <u>eating too much food</u> and <u>not getting enough exercise</u>.

3) Obesity can increase the risk of <u>diabetes</u>, <u>arthritis</u>, <u>heart disease</u> and <u>breast cancer</u>.

Body Mass Index Shows If You're Underweight or Overweight

1) The <u>Body Mass Index</u> (BMI) is used as a guide to help decide whether someone is <u>underweight</u>, <u>normal</u>, <u>overweight</u> or <u>obese</u>.

2) It's calculated from their <u>height</u> and <u>weight</u>:

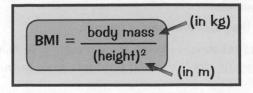

$$\text{BMI} = \frac{\text{body mass} \text{ (in kg)}}{(\text{height})^2 \text{ (in m)}}$$

Body Mass Index	Weight Description
below 18.5	underweight
18.5 - 24.9	normal
25 - 29.9	overweight
30 - 40	moderately obese
above 40	severely obese

The table shows how BMI is used to <u>classify</u> people's weight.

Your EAR for revision = 4.7534 hours...

What a cheery page. Make sure you know exactly how to use these pesky <u>equations</u>. You could end up having to calculate BMI or EAR in the exam. Pay attention to the units — <u>body mass</u> should always be in <u>kilograms</u>.

Infectious Disease

There really are loads of things out to get you, and you really do have to <u>fight attacks off</u> every day.

Infectious Diseases are Caused by Pathogens

1) An <u>infectious disease</u> is a disease that can be passed from one person to another (e.g. flu).
A <u>non-infectious disease</u> can't be passed on to another person (e.g. diabetes).

2) Infectious diseases are caused by <u>micro-organisms</u>.
Disease-causing micro-organisms are called <u>pathogens</u>. There are four main types:
- <u>FUNGI</u> — e.g. <u>athlete's foot</u> is caused by a fungus
- <u>BACTERIA</u> — e.g. <u>cholera</u> is caused by bacteria
- <u>PROTOZOA</u> (single-celled organisms) — e.g. <u>malaria</u> can be caused by protozoa.
- <u>VIRUSES</u> — e.g. <u>flu</u> is caused by a virus

3) The symptoms of an <u>infectious disease</u> are caused by <u>cell damage</u> or by <u>toxins</u> (poisons) produced by the pathogens.

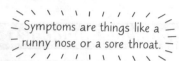
Symptoms are things like a runny nose or a sore throat.

4) <u>Genetic disorders</u> are non-infectious diseases. They're caused by <u>faulty genes</u>.

Malaria is an Example of an Infectious Disease

1) Malaria is caused by a <u>protozoan</u>. It's carried by <u>mosquitoes</u> — insects that feed on the blood of animals (including humans).

2) The protozoan is a <u>parasite</u> — an organism that <u>lives off</u> another organism. The other organism is called a <u>host</u>.

3) The mosquitoes are <u>vectors</u>. This means they <u>carry</u> the disease <u>without getting it</u> themselves.

4) Mosquitos <u>pick up</u> the malarial parasite when they <u>feed</u> on an <u>infected animal</u>. Every time the mosquito feeds on another animal it <u>passes the parasite on</u>.

Some Places Have a Higher Incidence of Disease

1) The incidence of a disease is <u>how often new cases occur</u> in a population in a set time, e.g. a year.

2) The incidence of many diseases is <u>higher</u> in:
- <u>hot places</u>, e.g. Africa, because pathogens reproduce faster in hot weather.
- <u>poor countries</u> because they don't have the <u>money</u> to <u>treat</u> diseases or <u>teach people</u> how to stop disease spreading.

The Body Has Four Main Ways of Keeping Out Pathogens

1) THE SKIN Undamaged skin <u>stops</u> pathogens <u>getting in</u>.

2) THE BLOOD If the skin gets damaged, <u>blood clots</u> form to <u>seal cuts</u> and keep the pathogens out.

3) THE STOMACH The stomach produces <u>hydrochloric acid</u>. This <u>kills</u> pathogens in food and drink.

4) THE AIRWAYS Your airways are lined with <u>sticky mucus</u> that traps <u>bacteria</u> before they reach the lungs.

Yawning is infectious — but it's not a disease thankfully...

You really do need to <u>learn</u> absolutely <u>everything</u> on this page. I can't think of a <u>single thing</u> that's not important.

Preventing and Treating Infectious Disease

An ounce of prevention is worth a pound of cure. That's what my mum says, anyhow.

Your Immune System Deals with Pathogens

1) If pathogens get into your body, your <u>immune system</u> kicks in. The most important part of your immune system is the <u>white blood cells</u>.

2) White blood cells travel around your <u>body</u> constantly <u>looking</u> for pathogens.

3) When they come across a pathogen they have <u>two lines of attack</u>:

1) Consuming Them

White blood cells can <u>engulf</u> (surround) pathogens and <u>digest</u> them.

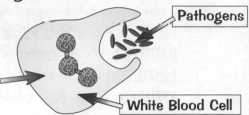

Pathogens

White Blood Cell

2) Producing Antibodies

1) Every pathogen has <u>molecules</u> on its <u>surface</u> called <u>antigens</u>.

2) When your white blood cells come across an <u>antigen</u> they'll start to produce <u>antibodies</u>.

3) Antibodies <u>lock on to</u> and <u>kill</u> the invading pathogens.

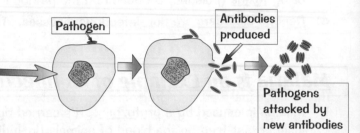

Pathogen

Antibodies produced

Pathogens attacked by new antibodies

Immunisation Stops You Getting Infections

1) When you're infected with a <u>new</u> pathogen it can take your white blood cells a while to produce the antibodies to deal with them. In that time you can get <u>very ill</u>, or maybe even die.

2) To avoid this you can be <u>immunised</u> (vaccinated) against some diseases, e.g. polio or measles. This stops you from getting the disease.

3) Immunisation is a type of <u>active immunity</u>:

- <u>ACTIVE</u> immunity is where the immune system <u>makes its own antibodies</u>.
- <u>PASSIVE</u> immunity is where you use <u>antibodies made by another organism</u>. E.g. antibodies are passed from mother to baby through breast milk.

You Can Take Antibiotics or Antivirals to Get Rid of Infections

1) <u>ANTIBIOTICS</u> are drugs that <u>kill bacteria</u>.

2) They can be used to <u>get rid of bacterial infections</u> that your body is having trouble with.

3) Antibiotics <u>don't kill viruses</u>.

4) <u>ANTIVIRALS</u> are drugs that <u>stop viruses</u> from <u>reproducing</u>. They can be used to treat <u>viral infections</u>.

5) Antivirals have <u>no effect</u> against <u>bacteria</u>.

I think I'm immune to revising...

There are a lot of 'anti's here, so make sure you don't get them confused. <u>Antigens</u> are what's on the surface of a pathogen, <u>antibodies</u> are what your blood cells make to fight off pathogens and <u>antibiotics</u> are a type of drug that kills bacteria. <u>Antivirals</u> are also drugs — but they work against viruses by stopping them from reproducing. Lovely.

Cancer and Drug Development

Ever wondered how drugs are developed? No, me either. But it's actually quite <u>interesting</u>.
First up though, a little bit on cancer.

You Can Reduce the Risk of Developing Some Cancers

Having a <u>healthy lifestyle</u> and <u>diet</u> can <u>reduce your risk</u> of getting some <u>cancers</u>.
For example:

- <u>Not smoking</u> reduces your chances of getting <u>lung cancer</u>.
- Eating <u>more fibre</u> may reduce your risk of getting <u>colon cancer</u>.

Drugs Developed to Treat Disease Need to be Tested

<u>New drugs</u> have to be <u>tested</u> before they can be used to make sure they're <u>safe</u> and that they <u>work</u>.
This is the usual way that drugs are developed and tested:

1) <u>Computer models</u> are often used first — these
   <u>predict</u> what a <u>human's response</u> will be to a drug.
2) The models can <u>identify</u> drugs that might be useful
   — so these can be tested in the next stage.

3) The drugs are then tested on <u>human tissues</u>.
4) You can't use human tissue to test drugs that affect <u>whole body systems</u> though.
   For example, testing a drug for <u>blood pressure</u> has to be done on a <u>whole animal</u>
   (because tissues don't have blood pressure).

5) The last step is to test the drug using <u>animals</u>.
6) Some people think it's <u>cruel</u> to test on animals, but others believe this is the
   <u>safest</u> way to make sure a drug isn't dangerous before it's given to humans.

7) After the drug has been tested on animals, it's
   tested on <u>humans</u> in a study called a <u>clinical trial</u>.
8) If it works and there are no harmful side effects
   in humans the drug is put on the market for sale.

My brother's an animal — they could test on him...

Make sure you learn all the stages in <u>testing</u> and <u>developing</u> a <u>drug</u> — you might get questioned on it in the exam.

Module B1 — Understanding Ourselves

Drugs: Use and Harm

Drugs (both the legal kind and the illegal kind) might be in the exam. So get reading.

Drugs Can be Beneficial or Harmful

1) Drugs are substances which change the way the body works.

2) Some drugs are useful, e.g. antibiotics. But many drugs are harmful if misused.

3) This is why you can buy some drugs over the counter at a pharmacy, but others you can only get on prescription — your doctor decides if you should have them.

4) Some people get addicted to drugs. This means they have a physical need for the drug.
If they don't get it they get withdrawal symptoms (e.g. shaking and vomiting).

5) Tolerance develops with some drugs. The body gets used to having it and so you need a higher dose to give the same effect.

6) If someone's addicted to a drug but wants to get off it, rehabilitation can help. This is where you get help and support to try and overcome an addiction.

You Need to Know All About These Drugs...

1) DEPRESSANTS — e.g. alcohol, solvents and temazepam.
These slow down the brain's activity.

2) STIMULANTS — e.g. nicotine, ecstasy, caffeine.
These increase the brain's activity.

3) PAINKILLERS — e.g. aspirin and paracetamol.
These block nerve impulses to reduce pain.

4) PERFORMANCE ENHANCERS — e.g. anabolic steroids.
These are sometimes taken by athletes because
they help build muscle. But they're banned by most sports organisations.

5) HALLUCINOGENS — e.g. LSD. They distort (change) what's seen and heard.

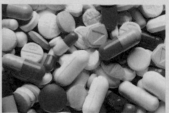

Some Drugs are Illegal

1) In the UK, illegal drugs are classified (grouped) into three main categories — Classes A, B and C.

2) Which class a drug is in depends on how dangerous it is — Class A drugs are the most dangerous.

3) Using or dealing Class A drugs is most serious — you could get a long prison sentence.

4) Being caught with Class C drugs will probably only get you a warning, although prison's still a possibility.

Drugs — they can cure you or kill you...

Many people take drugs of some kind, e.g. caffeine in coffee, alcohol, or an inhaler for asthma. Most of these are okay if you're careful with them and don't go overboard. It's misuse that can get you into trouble.

Smoking and Alcohol

Drinking a lot and smoking don't do you much good — and you need to know why for the exam...

Alcohol is a Depressant Drug

1) Alcohol's a <u>depressant</u> (see previous page) so it's main effect is to <u>decrease</u> the activity of the <u>brain</u>. This <u>slows</u> down the responses of the <u>nervous system</u>.

2) Being <u>drunk</u> is a <u>short-term effect</u> of alcohol. When you're drunk, you tend to have:
   - <u>impaired</u> (bad) <u>judgement</u>, <u>balance</u> and <u>muscle control</u>,
   - <u>slurred</u> speech, <u>blurred</u> vision, and <u>increased blood flow to the skin</u>.

   Being drunk also makes you <u>feel drowsy</u> (sleepy).

3) Your <u>reaction time</u> is <u>slower</u> when you <u>drink</u>, so you're <u>more likely</u> to have an <u>accident</u> if you drink and drive.

4) This is why you're <u>not allowed</u> to <u>drive</u> or fly a <u>plane</u> when you're drunk and why there are <u>legal limits</u> to the level of alcohol in the blood of <u>drivers</u> and <u>pilots</u>.

5) The <u>long-term effects</u> of drinking too much alcohol include <u>brain</u> and <u>liver</u> damage.

6) Doctors recommend you drink no more than <u>21 units of alcohol</u> each week if you're a <u>man</u>. They recommend you drink no more than <u>14 units</u> each week if you're a <u>woman</u>.

> Your reaction time is how long it takes you to respond to something you see or hear.

> <u>1 unit</u> = half a pint of average strength beer, 1 small glass of wine or 1 standard pub measure of spirits.

Burning Cigarettes Produce Four Main Things:

1) CARBON MONOXIDE — This <u>reduces</u> the amount of <u>oxygen</u> the blood can carry to the tissues, which can lead to <u>heart disease</u>.

2) NICOTINE — This is what makes smoking <u>addictive</u>.

3) TAR — This <u>covers the cilia</u> (little hairs in the airways) and causes <u>irritation</u>. Tar also contains <u>carcinogens</u> (substances that can <u>cause cancer</u>).

4) PARTICULATES — These are <u>small particles</u> that <u>build up</u> in the lung tissue, causing <u>irritation</u>.

Smoking Causes All Sorts of Illnesses

1) It causes <u>heart disease</u>.

2) It causes <u>cancer</u> of the <u>lung</u>, <u>throat</u>, <u>mouth</u> and <u>oesophagus</u>.

3) It causes <u>smoker's cough</u>. This is because:
   - Smoking damages the <u>cilia</u> on the <u>epithelial tissue</u> lining the <u>trachea</u>, <u>bronchi</u> and <u>bronchioles</u>.
   - The damaged cilia <u>can't get rid of mucus</u> properly.
   - The mucus <u>sticks</u> to air passages, making you to <u>cough more</u>.

4) Smoking also causes <u>bronchitis</u> and <u>emphysema</u>. Both these diseases make it difficult to breathe.

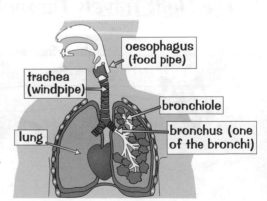

oesophagus (food pipe)

trachea (windpipe)

bronchiole

lung

bronchus (one of the bronchi)

Drinking and Smoking — it's not big and it's not clever...

You've probably guessed by now that <u>examiners</u> like questions on <u>interpreting data</u> — and you might get one to do with alcohol. It might look <u>tricky</u>, but all they're really asking is for you to <u>apply</u> what you know.

The Eye

Of all the <u>sense organs</u>, my personal favourite has to be the <u>eye</u>...

Learn the Eye with All Its Labels:

1) The <u>cornea refracts</u> (bends) light into the eye.

2) The <u>iris</u> controls <u>how much light</u> enters the <u>pupil</u> (the <u>hole</u> in the <u>middle</u>).

3) The <u>lens</u> also <u>refracts light</u>, <u>focusing</u> it onto the <u>retina</u>.

4) The <u>retina</u> is the <u>light sensitive</u> part.
   - It's covered in <u>receptors</u> that detect light.
   - Some of these receptors are sensitive to <u>light</u> of <u>different colours</u>.

5) The <u>optic nerve</u> carries impulses from the receptors to the <u>brain</u>.

6) The <u>blind spot</u> is where the optic nerve leaves your eye. There are <u>no receptors</u> there so it can't detect light.

7) Some people have <u>problems</u> with their <u>vision</u>, e.g. <u>red-green colour blindness</u> is due to a <u>lack</u> of certain specialised <u>cells</u> in the retina. Other problems include long-sightedness and short-sightedness (see next page).

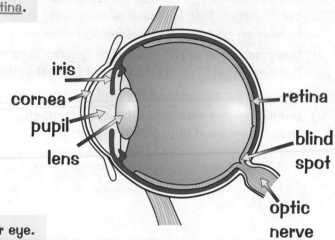

iris
cornea
pupil
lens
retina
blind spot
optic nerve

See page 28 for more on red-green colour blindness.

The Light Travels Through the Eye like This...

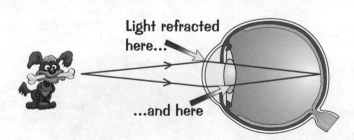

Light refracted here...

...and here

1) The light from the object is <u>refracted</u> (bent) into the eye by the <u>cornea</u>.

2) The <u>lens</u> refracts the light a bit more to <u>focus</u> it on your <u>retina</u>.

There's so much more than meets the eye here...

The eye is more than just the window to your soul — it's also a dead easy way to pick up marks in the exam. You just need to make sure you can <u>label</u> all its different <u>bits</u> and that you know what they <u>do</u>. Groovy.

Vision

If you thought that was it on the eye, you'd be wrong. This page is all about <u>vision</u> — <u>how the eye sees</u>...

Some People are Long-Sighted or Short-sighted

<u>LONG-SIGHTED</u> people <u>can't focus</u> on <u>NEAR</u> objects:

1) This happens when the <u>lens</u> is the <u>wrong shape</u> and doesn't <u>bend</u> the light enough, or the <u>eyeball</u> is too <u>short</u>.

2) The images of near objects are brought into focus <u>behind</u> the <u>retina</u>.

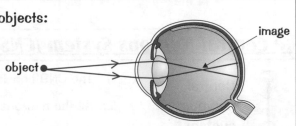

object   image

<u>SHORT-SIGHTED</u> people <u>can't focus</u> on <u>DISTANT</u> objects:

1) This happens when the <u>lens</u> is the <u>wrong shape</u> and bends the light <u>too much</u>, or the <u>eyeball</u> is too <u>long</u>.

2) The images of distant objects are brought into focus <u>in front</u> of the <u>retina</u>.

image

object

Binocular Vision Lets You Judge Depth

1) Some animals, including humans, see <u>objects</u> with <u>BOTH EYES</u> — this is called <u>BINOCULAR VISION</u>.

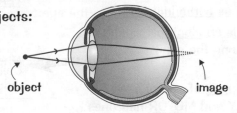

- When animals with binocular vision look at an object, their brain <u>compares</u> the images seen by each eye.

- The more <u>similarities</u> between the images, the <u>further away</u> the object.

- This means animals with binocular vision can <u>judge distances</u> well.

- But they have a <u>narrow field of vision</u>.

Your field of vision is how much you can see to your left and right.

2) Other animals, like turkeys and lizards, see <u>objects</u> with <u>ONE EYE</u> — this is called <u>MONOCULAR VISION</u>.

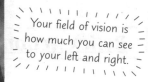

- Animals with monocular vision see <u>separate views</u> with each eye.

- This means they have a <u>wide field of vision</u>.

- But they <u>can't easily judge distance</u>.

I think I'm a little long-sighted...

If you can read this you've got better eyesight than me!

To see how important <u>binocular vision</u> is, cover one eye and try pouring water into a glass at arm's length.
That's why you never see turkeys or lizards pouring themselves a glass of orange squash.

Neurones and Reflexes

Ahh. The humble reflex. It might just save your life one day

Neurones Carry Information Around the Body

1) <u>Neurones</u> are nerve cells. They send information around the body as <u>nerve impulses</u>.

2) A nerve impulse is an <u>electrical signal</u>. It gets passed along the <u>axon</u> of the neurone.

3) There are <u>three types</u> of neurone — <u>SENSORY</u>, <u>RELAY</u> and <u>MOTOR</u> neurones.

LEARN THIS DIAGRAM of a typical **MOTOR NEURONE**:

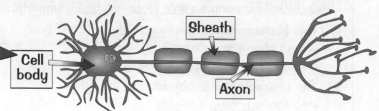

Cell body · Sheath · Axon

The Central Nervous System (CNS) Organises Information

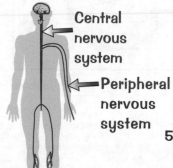

Central nervous system

Peripheral nervous system

1) The CNS consists of the <u>brain</u> and <u>spinal cord</u>.

2) All the neurones <u>outside</u> the CNS make up the <u>peripheral nervous system</u>.

3) A <u>change</u> in your environment is called a <u>stimulus</u>.

4) When you <u>detect</u> a stimulus, <u>receptors</u> (e.g. light receptors in the eye) generate a <u>nerve impulse</u>. This travels along <u>sensory neurones</u> to the <u>CNS</u>.

5) The CNS then sends information to an <u>effector</u> (<u>muscle</u> or <u>gland</u>) along a <u>motor neurone</u>. The effector then responds to the information.

6) <u>Voluntary responses</u> (the things you decide to do) are under the <u>conscious control</u> of the brain — this means you have to <u>think</u> about doing them.

Reflex Actions Stop You Injuring Yourself

1) <u>Reflex actions</u> are <u>automatic</u> (done without thinking) so they're <u>very fast</u>.

2) The <u>conscious brain isn't</u> involved in a <u>reflex arc</u>. The <u>sensory neurone</u> connects to a <u>relay neurone</u> in the <u>spinal cord</u>.

3) The relay neurone links <u>directly</u> to the correct <u>motor neurone</u>.

4) Reflex actions have a <u>protective role</u>, e.g. pulling back your hand when you touch a <u>burning hot</u> plate.

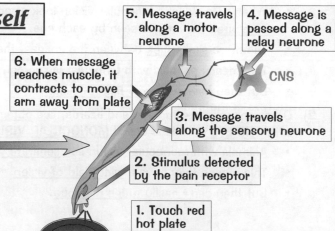

5. Message travels along a motor neurone

4. Message is passed along a relay neurone

6. When message reaches muscle, it contracts to move arm away from plate

CNS

3. Message travels along the sensory neurone

2. Stimulus detected by the pain receptor

1. Touch red hot plate

Don't get all twitchy — just learn it...

There are loads of different <u>reflexes</u>. But the good thing is that they all follow the <u>same pathway</u> — so you just need to learn this once. Here it is:

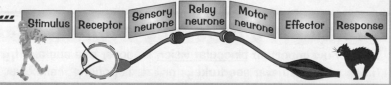

Stimulus · Receptor · Sensory neurone · Relay neurone · Motor neurone · Effector · Response

Module B1 — Understanding Ourselves

Homeostasis

Homeostasis involves balancing body functions to maintain a 'constant internal environment'. Smashing.

Homeostasis is Maintaining a Constant Internal Environment

1) Conditions in your body are kept <u>steady</u> by <u>automatic control systems</u>.

2) They're kept steady so that your <u>cells</u> can function at their <u>optimum</u> (best) level.

3) Homeostasis involves balancing <u>inputs</u> (stuff going into your body) with <u>outputs</u> (stuff leaving).

4) <u>Water content</u>, <u>body temperature</u> and <u>carbon dioxide level</u> are all maintained by homeostasis.

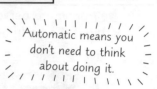
Automatic means you don't need to think about doing it.

Core Body Temperature is 37 °C

1) All <u>enzymes</u> have an <u>optimum temperature</u> — this is the temperature they <u>work best</u> at. For enzymes in the human body it's about <u>37 °C</u>.

2) Your body does these things to keep it at the right temperature:

When You're TOO HOT:

1) <u>Lots of sweat</u> is produced — when sweat <u>evaporates</u> it uses heat from the skin. This transfers heat from your skin to the environment, which <u>cools you down</u>.

2) <u>More blood</u> flows near the <u>surface</u> of the skin so more heat can be lost to the surroundings.

> If you get <u>too hot</u> you can get:
> * <u>dehydrated</u>
> * <u>heat stroke</u>
>
> These conditions can <u>kill</u> you.

When You're TOO COLD:

1) <u>Very little sweat</u> is produced.

2) <u>Less blood</u> flows near the <u>surface</u> of the skin so that less heat is lost to the surroundings.

3) <u>Shivering</u> produces heat through respiration.

4) <u>Exercising</u> warms you up in the same way.

5) Adding <u>extra clothes</u> helps keep your body warm.

> * Your body temperature can drop dangerously if you stay out in the <u>cold</u> for a <u>long time</u>.
> * This is called <u>hypothermia</u>.
> * If you don't get help quickly you can <u>die</u>.

You can Measure Body Temperature in Different Ways

1) Doctors sometimes measure your <u>body temperature</u> to check <u>how well you are</u>.

2) You can measure the temperature of your <u>ear</u>, <u>finger</u>, <u>mouth</u> or <u>anus</u> to find out what your body temperature is.

3) You can <u>measure</u> your temperature using:

* A <u>clinical thermometer</u> — this is a glass tube full of alcohol.
* <u>Temperature-sensitive strips</u> change colour depending on how hot you are.
* <u>Digital thermometers</u> use a digital probe connected to a read-out display.
* <u>Thermal imaging</u> isn't used to measure temperature normally, but is sometimes used to look for cancer, e.g. a breast cancer can be seen because it's hotter than the surrounding tissue.

Keep your cool — learn about homeostasis...

If you're in really high temperatures for a long time you can get <u>heat stroke</u> — and if you don't cool down it can kill you. Fortunately, good old British drizzle means that heat stroke needn't worry most of us. Phew.

Controlling Blood Sugar

Blood sugar level is controlled using the hormone insulin. It's an example of homeostasis. Learn how it works.

Insulin Controls Blood Sugar Level

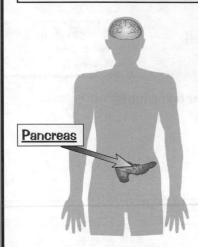

Pancreas

1) Insulin is a hormone that controls the amount of sugar in the blood.

2) Eating foods that contain carbohydrates causes the amount of sugar in the blood to increase.

3) Respiration causes the amount of sugar in the blood to decrease.

4) Insulin is produced by an organ called the pancreas.

Hormones are chemicals used to send information around the body.

Here's how insulin keeps blood sugar steady...

- If the blood sugar level gets TOO HIGH, insulin is RELEASED by the pancreas. This lowers the blood sugar level.

- If the blood sugar level gets TOO LOW, insulin is NOT RELEASED.

5) Hormones like insulin are carried in the blood to other parts of the body.

6) They travel all over the body but only affect particular organs, called target organs.

7) Travelling by blood is slow. This is why the body reacts to hormones more slowly than it does to nervous impulses (which are very quick — see page 20).

Having Diabetes Means You Can't Control Your Blood Sugar Level

Diabetes is a condition that affects your ability to control your blood sugar level. There are two types:

Type 1 Diabetes

1) Type 1 diabetes is where the pancreas can't produce insulin.

2) The result is that a person's blood sugar can rise to a level that can kill them.

3) People with type 1 diabetes can partly control the condition by having a carefully controlled diet (see below).

4) They also need insulin therapy, which usually involves injecting insulin into the blood several times a day (often at mealtimes).

Type 2 Diabetes

1) Type 2 diabetes is where a person can't respond to insulin properly. This can also cause blood sugar level to rise to a dangerous level.

2) Type 2 diabetes is usually just controlled by limiting the amount of sugary foods that are eaten. These cause the blood sugar level to rise rapidly.

Diabetes — it's no joke...

Remember: insulin is released to lower the blood sugar level when it gets too high. And don't forget that there are two types of diabetes either — you need to learn the different ways of controlling them.

Plant Hormones and Growth

Just like animals, plants <u>respond</u> to changes in their <u>environment</u>. A plant <u>growth response</u> is called a <u>tropism</u>.

Auxins are Plant Growth Hormones

1) <u>Plant growth</u> is controlled by <u>hormones</u> called plant growth hormones.

2) They control the growth of <u>shoots</u> and <u>roots</u>, <u>flowering</u> and the <u>ripening of fruit</u>.

3) The plant hormones that control the <u>growth</u> of <u>shoots</u> and <u>roots</u> are called <u>auxins</u>.
   They move through the plant in <u>solution</u> (dissolved in water).

4) Auxins are involved in the growth responses of plants to <u>light</u> (phototropism) and <u>gravity</u> (geotropism).

Auxins Change the Direction of Root and Shoot Growth

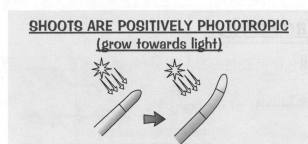

SHOOTS ARE POSITIVELY PHOTOTROPIC
(grow towards light)

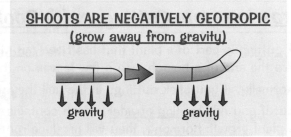

SHOOTS ARE NEGATIVELY GEOTROPIC
(grow away from gravity)

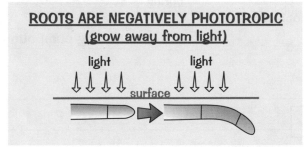

ROOTS ARE NEGATIVELY PHOTOTROPIC
(grow away from light)

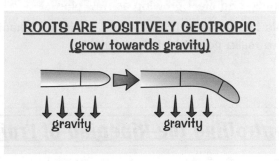

ROOTS ARE POSITIVELY GEOTROPIC
(grow towards gravity)

1) Plants <u>need light</u> to make their own <u>food</u> through <u>photosynthesis</u>.
   If plants don't get enough light, they <u>die</u>.

2) So plant shoots grow towards the light to <u>increase</u> the <u>plant's chances</u> of <u>survival</u>.

3) Plants also need <u>water</u>. Plant <u>roots grow downwards</u> to reach water in the <u>soil</u>.

This Experiment Shows That Shoots Grow Towards Light

1) Place a plant inside a <u>cardboard box</u>, with a <u>hole</u> in <u>one</u> side, as shown.

2) If you leave the plant for a <u>few days</u> you'll notice that the shoots will start to bend and <u>grow towards the light</u>.

3) You also need a <u>control</u> (see page 3). This is used to show that there are <u>no other factors</u> making the plant bend.

4) The control should be a plant <u>surrounded by light</u> on all sides. This plant <u>shouldn't bend</u> at all.

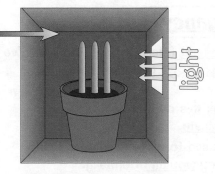

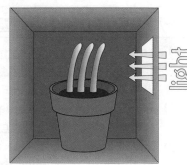

A plant auxin to a bar — 'ouch'...

Shoots grow towards light and roots grow towards gravity — that's not <u>too hard</u> to remember, now, is it.

Commercial Use of Plant Hormones

Plant hormones can be used to speed up or slow down plant growth.
This means they can be used for all sorts of useful things...

1) As Selective Weedkillers

1) Selective weedkillers are plant growth hormones that only affect weeds.

2) The weedkillers change the weeds' normal growth patterns, which soon kills them.

3) Grass and crops aren't affected by these weedkillers.

Unhappy weeds

2) Growing from Cuttings with Rooting Powder

1) A cutting is part of a plant that has been cut off it, like the end of a branch with a few leaves on it.

2) Normally, if you stick cuttings in the soil they won't grow.

3) But if you add rooting powder, which contains a plant growth hormone, they will produce roots rapidly and start growing as new plants.

4) This lets growers produce lots of clones (exact copies) of a really good plant very quickly.

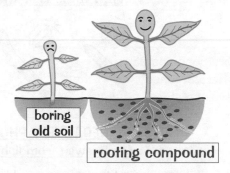

boring old soil

rooting compound

3) Controlling the Ripening of Fruit

1) Plant hormones can be used to delay the ripening of fruits.

2) This allows the fruit to be picked while it's still unripe. (This means it's firmer and less easily damaged).

3) Ripening hormone is then added and the fruit will ripen on the way to the supermarket — so it's perfect just as it reaches the shelves.

4) Controlling Dormancy

1) Lots of seeds won't germinate (start growing) until they've been through certain conditions, e.g. a period of cold. This is called dormancy.

2) Plant hormones can break this dormancy and cause seeds to germinate.

3) These hormones can be used to make seeds germinate at times of year when they wouldn't normally.

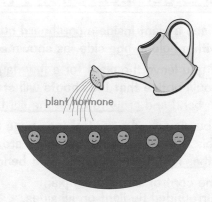

plant hormone

You will ripen when I SAY you can ripen — and NOT BEFORE...

The hormone used to make fruit ripen on the way to the supermarket is given off by bananas. So if you've got some fruit you want ripening, just put it in a bag with a banana. Now, don't say I never tell you anything useful.

Genes and Chromosomes

This page is a bit tricky, but it's dead important that you get to grips with all the stuff on it — because you're going to hear a lot more about it over the next few pages...

1) Most cells in your body have a <u>nucleus</u>. The nucleus contains your <u>genetic information</u> in the form of <u>chromosomes</u>.

2) In most animal cells chromosomes come in <u>pairs</u>. Different species have a different <u>number of pairs</u>. A human body cell nucleus contains <u>23 pairs of chromosomes</u>.

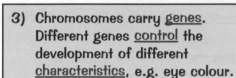

nucleus

A single <u>chromosome</u>.

A <u>pair</u> of <u>chromosomes</u>. (They're always in pairs, one from each <u>parent</u>.)

3) Chromosomes carry <u>genes</u>. Different genes <u>control</u> the development of different <u>characteristics</u>, e.g. eye colour.

DNA molecule

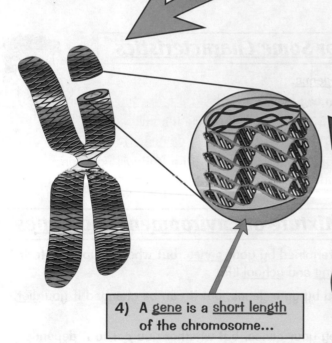

4) A <u>gene</u> is a <u>short length</u> of the chromosome...

5) ...which is quite a long length of <u>DNA</u>.

It's hard being a DNA molecule, there's so much to remember...

This is the bare bones of genetics, so you definitely need to understand <u>everything</u> on this page or you'll find the rest of this topic dead hard. The best way to get all of these important facts stuck in your head is to <u>cover</u> the page, <u>scribble</u> down the main points and <u>sketch</u> out the diagrams...

Genes and the Environment

Some of your characteristics are determined by your <u>genes</u>. Some of your characteristics are determined by the <u>environment</u>. But most of your characteristics are determined by <u>both</u>.

Genes Are Responsible For Certain Characteristics

1) Some characteristics are controlled by your <u>genes</u>, e.g. eye colour.
2) There can be <u>different versions</u> of the <u>same gene</u>. These are called <u>ALLELES</u>.
3) Alleles result in different versions of the same <u>characteristic</u>, e.g. blue or brown eyes.
4) Everybody has <u>different combinations</u> of alleles — this is called <u>genetic variation</u> (see next page for what causes it).

Characteristics Can Be Dominant or Recessive

1) Children <u>inherit</u> some <u>characteristics</u> from their parents, like their eye colour.
2) Some characteristics are <u>dominant</u> over others. For example, brown eyes are dominant over blue eyes.
3) Blue eyes are a <u>recessive</u> characteristic.
4) Recessive characteristics are <u>only seen</u> when there are <u>no dominant characteristics</u> to inherit.
5) In the exam you might be given some <u>results</u> from a <u>breeding experiment</u> and asked to figure out which characteristic is dominant and which one is recessive.
6) If <u>most</u> of the offspring have the <u>same characteristic</u>, e.g. brown eyes, then that's the <u>dominant</u> characteristic.

Your Environment is Responsible for Some Characteristics

1) Your characteristics <u>aren't all</u> controlled by your <u>genes</u>.
2) Your <u>environment</u> is responsible for <u>some</u> of them, e.g. scars.

Most Characteristics are Due to a Mixture of Environment and Genes

1) <u>INTELLIGENCE</u> — your <u>maximum IQ</u> might be determined by your <u>genes</u>, but whether you get to it depends on your environment, e.g. your <u>upbringing</u> and <u>school</u> life.
2) <u>BODY MASS</u> — your <u>natural weight</u> is determined by your genes, but it can be changed if you <u>diet</u>, or <u>eat loads of junk food</u>.
3) <u>HEIGHT</u> — your <u>maximum height</u> is determined by your genes, but whether you get to it depends on your environment. E.g. if you don't get enough food when you're little, you won't be as tall as you could have been.

My mum's got no trousers — cos I've got her jeans...

Remember that most <u>characteristics</u> can be determined by <u>both genes and the environment</u>. And make sure you learn the three <u>examples</u> at the bottom of the page — you could well get asked about them in the exam.

Causes of Genetic Variation

Everyone (except identical twins) has <u>different genes</u> to everyone else. This page is all about why...

There are Three Things That Cause Genetic Variation

① Gamete Formation — *Making Sperm Cells and Egg Cells*

1) Gametes are <u>sperm cells</u> and <u>egg cells</u>.

2) They're formed in the <u>ovaries</u> or <u>testes</u>.

3) The body cells they're made from have <u>23 pairs</u> of chromosomes.

4) In each pair there's one chromosome that was <u>originally inherited</u> from <u>mum</u>, and one that was inherited from <u>dad</u>.

5) When these body cells <u>split</u> to form gametes, the chromosomes are also <u>split up</u>.

6) So gametes end up with <u>half</u> the number of chromosomes of a normal body cell — just <u>23</u>.

7) In each gamete, some of your <u>dad's</u> chromosomes are grouped with some from your <u>mum</u>.

8) This shuffling up of chromosomes leads to <u>variation</u> in the new generation.

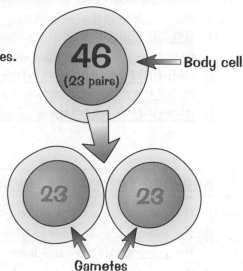

Body cell

Gametes

② Fertilisation — *the Gametes Join Together*

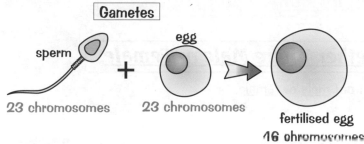

Gametes

sperm

egg

+ →

23 chromosomes   23 chromosomes

fertilised egg
46 chromosomes
(23 pairs)

1) Fertilisation is when the <u>sperm</u> and the <u>egg</u> join to form a new cell.

2) The sperm and the egg have <u>23 chromosomes each</u>. They join to make a cell with the full <u>46 chromosomes</u>.

3) But fertilisation is <u>random</u> — you don't know which two gametes are going to join together. This produces <u>variation</u>.

③ Mutations — *Changes to the Genetic Code*

1) Occasionally a gene may <u>mutate</u> — this just means that it <u>changes</u>.

2) This can create <u>new characteristics</u>, <u>increasing variation</u>.

Revise this page for a bit of variation...

So <u>variation</u> is created when a mixture of chromosomes is randomly shuffled into <u>gametes</u>. Then a random gamete fuses with another random gamete at <u>fertilisation</u> to create more variation (oh, the romance of it all).

Genetic Disorders and Sex Inheritance

There's been a lot to learn about genes. This is the last page though, I promise. There's a bit more about chromosomes to finish off too, then you can start the lovely Revision Summary questions.

Genetic Disorders are Caused by Faulty Genes

Faulty genes (genes that don't work properly) are responsible for genetic disorders. Here are some examples:

1) CYSTIC FIBROSIS is where the body produces a lot of thick sticky mucus in the air passages and pancreas.
2) RED-GREEN COLOUR BLINDNESS is where the sufferer finds it hard to tell the difference between red and green.
3) SICKLE CELL ANAEMIA is where the red blood cells are the wrong shape.

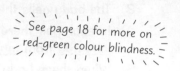
See page 18 for more on red-green colour blindness.

Knowing There are Genetic Disorders in Your Family Can Raise Difficult Issues

1) If a person finds out they're going to get ill in the future, it can be hard for them to deal with.
2) If a person knows their children might inherit a genetic disorder, it could affect whether they choose to have children.
3) If a parent finds out their unborn baby has a genetic disorder, they may feel they can't cope or the child will suffer too much. They might decide to have an abortion.

Your Chromosomes Control Whether You're Male or Female

1) Two chromosomes decide whether you turn out male or female.
2) These chromosomes are labelled X and Y.

> * All women have two X chromosomes: XX
> * The XX combination causes female characteristics.

> * All men have an X and a Y chromosome: XY
> * The Y chromosome causes male characteristics.

Congratulations! It's an XX.

3) This is true for all mammals, but not for some other organisms, e.g. plants.

Have you got the Y-Factor...

Right, that's about it for genes. Remember that the genes you inherit from your parents determine some of your characteristics. But sometimes you can inherit faulty genes and these can cause disorders. Some disorders people can live with, like being red-green colour blind. But others, like cystic fibrosis, are pretty nasty.

Revision Summary for Module B1

That was a long section, but kind of interesting, I reckon. These questions will show what you know and what you don't... if you get stuck, have a look back to remind yourself. But before the exam, make sure you can do all of them without any help — that's the only way you'll know you're ready.

1) What's the difference between 'fit' and 'healthy'?

2) Describe what's meant by the term 'systolic pressure'.

3) Explain one way that smoking can increase blood pressure.

4) How do narrow arteries increase the risk of a heart attack?

5) What does the body need carbohydrates for?

6) Give three reasons why people choose to eat different diets.

7) Explain what causes the condition called kwashiorkor.
   Why is this condition more common in developing countries?

8) Name three health problems that obesity can increase the risk of.

9) Describe the four main ways the body has of keeping out pathogens.

10) Explain how white blood cells destroy pathogens.

11) Give two ways to reduce the risk of developing some cancers.

12) Explain why drugs have to be tested before they can be used.

13) Why can you only get some drugs on prescription?

14) What does a depressant do? Give one example of a depressant.

15) Give one long-term effect of drinking too much alcohol.

16) Explain why smoking can give you a 'smoker's cough'.

17) What does the cornea do?

18) Describe the path of light through the eye.

19) Give one advantage and one disadvantage of monocular vision.

20) Draw a diagram of a typical motor neurone, labelling all its parts.

21) Describe the path taken by a reflex arc.

22) Name three things that need to be kept steady by homeostasis.

23) Describe how body temperature is reduced when you're too hot.

24) Explain how insulin controls blood sugar level.

25) What is the difference between how type 1 and type 2 diabetes are usually controlled?

26) What are auxins?

27) Give three ways that plant growth hormones are used commercially.

28) How many pairs of chromosomes are there in most human body cells?

29) Explain why your height is a result of a mixture of your genes and your environment.

30) Name three sources of genetic variation.

31) Give three examples of genetic disorders.

32) Which chromosomes determine your sex?

Module C1 — Carbon Chemistry

Atoms, Molecules and Compounds

Here we go then... <u>atoms</u> are the building blocks that everything is made from. Everything.

Atoms are a Type of Particle

1) Atoms are <u>really tiny</u> — they're <u>too small to see</u>.
2) They have a <u>nucleus</u> in the middle.
3) Tiny particles called <u>electrons</u> move <u>around</u> the nucleus.
4) The <u>electrons</u> are <u>negatively</u> charged.

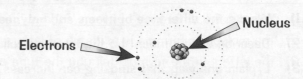

Nucleus

Electrons

Atoms Can Join Together to Make Molecules

1) When atoms are <u>joined together</u> they make <u>molecules</u>.
   E.g. oxygen molecules are made from two oxygen atoms joined together.

   Ⓞ = Oxygen atom   ⓄⓄ = Oxygen molecule

2) An <u>element</u> is a substance that has only <u>one type</u> of atom — so oxygen is an element.

3) A <u>compound</u> is a substance made up of <u>different types</u> of atom.
   E.g. carbon dioxide molecules are made from two oxygen atoms and a carbon atom joined together.

   Ⓞ = Oxygen atom   Ⓒ = Carbon atom   ⓄⒸⓄ = Carbon dioxide molecule

Atoms Are Joined Together by Bonds

The <u>electrons</u> in an atom can make <u>chemical bonds</u>.
There are two types of bond you need to know about.

COVALENT BONDS
1) Sometimes atoms can <u>share a pair of electrons</u>.
2) This is called <u>covalent bonding</u>.

IONIC BONDS
1) Atoms can also <u>give electrons</u> to other atoms.
2) If an atom <u>gives away</u> an electron it becomes <u>positively charged</u> (+).
3) If an atom <u>gets</u> an electron it becomes <u>negatively charged</u> (−).
4) Charged atoms are called <u>ions</u>.
5) If a <u>positive ion</u> meets a <u>negative ion</u> they'll be <u>attracted</u> to one another.
   This attraction is called an <u>ionic bond</u>.

The electron on the Na is given to the Cl.

So, Na has a positive charge and Cl has a negative charge. They are held together by an ionic bond.

Don't panic — it's only a bunch of letters and numbers...

It's easy to tell <u>atoms</u>, <u>molecules</u> and <u>ions</u> apart. Atoms are shown as one letter, e.g. O or C, molecules have more than one atom, e.g. CO or H_2O and ions are shown with a charge, e.g. Na^+, H^+ or Ca^{2+}.

Chemical Formulas

Scientists use <u>formulas</u> to show different molecules. There are two types of formula you need to know about...

The Molecular Formula Tells You What Atoms There Are

1) You can tell what <u>kind of atoms</u> and <u>how many</u> there are in a substance by looking at its <u>molecular formula</u>.

2) The molecular formula is made up of <u>letters and numbers</u>. E.g. H_2O, CH_4, HCl are all molecular formulas.

3) The <u>letters</u> in the formula tell you the type of <u>atoms</u> it's made up of.

4) The little <u>number</u> at the bottom tells you <u>how many</u> of that atom there are.

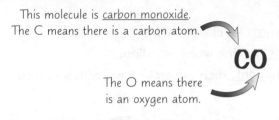

This molecule is <u>carbon monoxide</u>.
The C means there is a carbon atom.

CO

The O means there
is an oxygen atom.

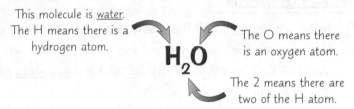

This molecule is <u>water</u>.
The H means there is a
hydrogen atom.

H₂O

The O means there
is an oxygen atom.

The 2 means there are
two of the H atom.

The Displayed Formula Shows How the Atoms are Arranged

1) You can draw out <u>pictures</u> that show the <u>atoms</u> and the <u>bonds</u> in different molecules.

2) These are called <u>displayed formulas</u>. For example:

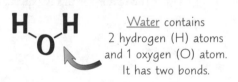

H–O–H

<u>Water</u> contains
2 hydrogen (H) atoms
and 1 oxygen (O) atom.
It has two bonds.

<u>Methane</u> contains
1 carbon (C) atom and
4 hydrogen (H) atoms.
It has four bonds.

```
  H
  |
H–C–H
  |
  H
```

Some Formulas Have Brackets

1) Don't panic if the molecular formula has <u>brackets</u> in it. They're easy too.
    For example: $CH_3(CH_2)_2CH_3$

    The 2 after the bracket means that there are 2 lots of CH_2.

2) Drawing the <u>displayed formula</u> of the compound
    is a good way to count up the number of atoms.

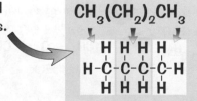

$CH_3(CH_2)_2CH_3$

```
  H H H H
  | | | |
H–C–C–C–C–H
  | | | |
  H H H H
```

3) So, altogether there are <u>4 carbon atoms</u> and <u>10 hydrogen atoms</u> in this molecule.

4) You might need to write out the <u>molecular formula</u> from the <u>displayed formula</u>.

5) It's easy — just <u>count up</u> the number of <u>each type of atom</u> and write it as above, e.g. CH_4, H_2O.
    Even better... you can write $CH_3(CH_2)_2CH_3$ as C_4H_{10}.

AHHHH — more letters and numbers...

Okay, I admit it — this is a pretty <u>dull</u> page. But it's easy. So be grateful for that. The only way to make sure
you know your displayed and molecular formulas is to practise them over and over.

Chemical Equations

If you're going to get anywhere in chemistry you need to know about chemical equations...

Chemical Equations Show What Happens in a Reaction

1) In a chemical reaction chemicals react together to make new chemicals.
2) The chemicals that react are called reactants. The chemicals that are made are called products.
3) Scientists use equations to show what happens in chemical reactions.

Word Equations

1) In a word equation all the chemicals are written out as words — clever that.
2) If you know the reactants and the products you can write out the word equation.
3) You put the reactants on the left and the products on the right, then separate them with an arrow.
   For example:

These are the reactants.   methane + oxygen → carbon dioxide + water   These are the products.

Symbol Equations

1) These are just like word equations but the chemicals are shown using molecular formulas.
2) For example, the symbol equation for the word equation above is:

$$CH_4 + 2O_2 \rightarrow CO_2 + 2H_2O$$

You may have spotted that there's a '2' in front of the O_2 and the H_2O. The reason for this is explained below...

Symbol Equations Need to be Balanced

1) You balance equations by putting numbers in front of the molecules so there are the same number of each type of atom on each side of the arrow.
2) But you can't change numbers in the molecular formulas. So changing O_2 to O_3 is a no-no.
3) Start by putting a number in front of one of the molecules to balance that type of atom. Then keep doing it until they all balance. For example:

1 $CH_4 + O_2 \rightarrow CO_2 + H_2O$
1C, 4H, 2O   1C, 2H, 3O

2 There aren't enough H's on the right. So, add a 2 in front of the H_2O.
$CH_4 + O_2 \rightarrow CO_2 + 2H_2O$
1C, 4H, 2O   1C, 4H, 4O

3 Now there aren't enough O's on the left. So, add a 2 in front of the O_2.
$CH_4 + 2O_2 \rightarrow CO_2 + 2H_2O$
1C, 4H, 4O   1C, 4H, 4O

The equation is not balanced — there are different numbers of hydrogen and oxygen atoms on each side of the equation.

Hooray. The equation is now balanced — there is the same number of each type of atom on both sides of the equation.

It's all about getting the balance right...

Balancing equations isn't as bad as it looks. Just add a number in front of a molecule to balance one type of atom and then work out the numbers again. Keep going until the number of each type of atom on both sides is the same.

Food Additives

All sorts of additives get put in food — they're used to make the food <u>look better</u>, <u>taste better</u> or <u>last longer</u>.

Additives Make Food Last Longer and Look and Taste Better

1) <u>Additives</u> are <u>chemicals</u> added to food to <u>improve it</u>.
2) There are <u>four</u> types of additive you need to know about.

Food Colours

1) <u>Food colours</u> improve the colour of food.
2) They're often used in sweets and soft drinks.

Flavour Enhancers

1) <u>Flavour enhancers</u> improve the <u>taste and smell</u> of food.
2) They're often added to packet soups, sausages and ready meals.

Antioxidants

1) When some foods react with <u>oxygen</u> in the air, they <u>go off</u>.
2) For example, <u>slices of apple</u> go <u>brown</u> because molecules in the apple are reacting with the air.
3) <u>Antioxidants</u> are added to foods to <u>stop</u> them reacting with oxygen.
4) Sausages, bread, jam and instant soup often have antioxidants added to them. So now you know.

Emulsifiers

1) If you put <u>oil</u> and <u>water</u> in a glass they'll <u>separate</u> out into <u>two layers</u>.

2) This is because oil and water <u>don't mix</u>.

3) <u>Emulsifiers</u> help water and oil to <u>mix</u> and <u>not separate</u>.

4) Emulsifiers are molecules with <u>two parts</u>:

emulsifier molecule

hydrophilic (likes water)   hydrophobic (likes oil)

- One part of the emulsifier molecule is <u>water loving</u> — this is called the <u>hydrophilic</u> part.
- One part of the emulsifier molecule is <u>oil or fat loving</u> — this is called the <u>hydrophobic</u> part.

5) So emulsifier molecules go <u>between</u> water molecules and oil molecules and hold them <u>together</u>.

6) <u>Mayonnaise</u>, <u>low-fat spread</u> and <u>ice cream</u> all contain emulsifiers.

Add me to food and it'll disappear...

The long-term effects of some additives aren't known. A lot of food manufacturers now make additive-free products for people who don't want to take the risk. There is, as yet, <u>no additive-free exam</u> though. So you'll need to learn this page — food colours, flavour enhancers, antioxidants and emulsifiers, hydrophilic bits and all.

Cooking and Chemical Change

This is a page about irreversible chemical changes. When you cook things, the chemical structure of the substance changes, and it can't change back. (In my case, cooking and burning are similar processes.)

Cooking Causes Chemical Changes

1) Cooking food needs energy (i.e. heat) and produces new substances.
2) Once you've cooked something, you can't change it back. The cooking process is irreversible.
3) This means a chemical change has taken place.

Eggs and Meat

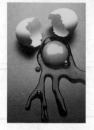

1) Eggs and meat are good sources of protein.
2) Protein molecules change shape when you heat them. This is called denaturing.
3) It changes the texture of the food and makes it easier to digest.
4) It also makes the food change in appearance, e.g. egg whites change from colourless to white.

Baking Powder Breaks Down When Heated

1) When you heat baking powder, it breaks down (decomposes) into other substances.
2) Baking powder contains the chemical sodium hydrogencarbonate. You need to know the equation for what happens when it's heated:

sodium hydrogencarbonate → sodium carbonate + carbon dioxide + water
$$2NaHCO_3 \rightarrow Na_2CO_3 + CO_2 + H_2O$$

3) Baking powder is used in baking cakes — the carbon dioxide produced makes the cake rise.
4) You can check that it is actually carbon dioxide that has been formed by using a chemical test:

Carbon dioxide can be detected using limewater — if you bubble carbon dioxide through limewater the limewater will go cloudy.

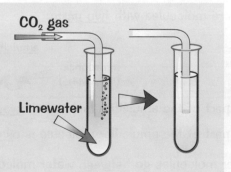

CO$_2$ gas

Limewater

You'll need to learn this page for your eggsam...

Cooking is a kind of chemistry — when you cook something, you're causing a chemical change. The changes are irreversible, as you'll know if you've ever tried to unscramble an egg.

Paints and Pigments

You might just think of paint as brightly coloured stuff — but there's a lot of chemistry that goes into making your bedroom walls lime green.

Pigments Give Paints Their Colours

Paint usually contains three different bits: solvent, binding medium and pigment.

1) The pigment gives the paint its colour.

2) The binding medium is a liquid that sticks the pigment to the surface you've painted.

3) The solvent thins the paint and makes it easier to spread.

Paints are Colloids

1) A colloid is a mixture of really tiny particles of one kind of stuff mixed in with another kind of stuff.

2) They're mixed in, but not dissolved, so we say they're dispersed.

3) A paint is a colloid where particles of a pigment are dispersed through a liquid.

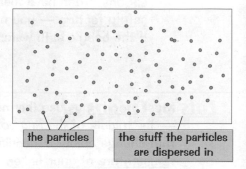

the particles

the stuff the particles are dispersed in

Some Paints are Water-based and Some are Oil-based

1) You can use paint to protect things (like wooden window frames) or to decorate them.

2) You usually put paint on in a thin layer.

3) The paint dries as the solvent evaporates.

4) Depending on the type of job you're doing, you might choose an emulsion paint or an oil-based paint.

1) Emulsion paints are water-based — the solvent used in these paints is water.

2) Emulsion paints dry when the water evaporates.

1) Oil paints are oil-based.

2) The pigment is dispersed in an oil.

3) The solvent is something that'll dissolve the oil.

The world was black and white before the 1950s — I saw it on TV...

There are heaps of different types of paint — and some are more suitable for certain jobs than others. Like if you're repainting your car, emulsions are definitely not the way to go — they'll wash off in the rain. And likewise if you painted your little sister's face with oil paint, your mum would probably ground you for a year.

Special Pigments

If you thought the science behind brightly coloured <u>paint</u> was clever, wait till you read about the <u>pigments</u> on this page. They can <u>change colour</u> and even **glow in the dark**...

Thermochromic Pigments Change Colour When Heated

Thermochromic pigments <u>change colour</u> when heated or cooled.
There are lots of clever <u>uses</u> for <u>thermochromic pigments</u>:

Thermochromic pigments are used in <u>fancy electric kettles</u> that <u>change colour</u> as the water boils.

They're used on <u>drinks mugs</u> to warn you when the contents are <u>too hot</u> to drink.

Baby products, like <u>bath toys</u> and <u>baby spoons</u>, often have them added as a <u>safety feature</u> — you can tell easily if the baby's bath water or food is <u>too hot</u>.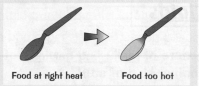

Food at right heat   Food too hot

Most <u>mood rings</u> use thermochromic pigments — the middle of the ring contains <u>pigments</u> that change colour depending on the <u>temperature of your finger</u>.

(And you thought it was all to do with how **calm** or how **passionate** you were...)

Phosphorescent Pigments Glow in the Dark

1) Phosphorescent pigments <u>absorb light</u> and <u>store the energy</u>.

2) This energy is <u>released</u> as <u>light</u> over a period of time — from a few seconds to a couple of hours.

3) This means phosphorescent pigments <u>glow in the dark</u>.

4) An obvious use is a <u>watch</u> or <u>clock</u> with glow-in-the-dark hands.

Thermochromic pigments — the truth behind mood rings...

For a brief spell in the early 1990s colour-changing T-shirts were reeeeally cool. Although I was never quite sure why you'd want to show the world just how hot and sweaty your armpits were.
Glow-in-the-dark erasers too... I mean... when do you <u>ever</u> need to rub out mistakes in the dark?

Polymers

Polymers are things like plastic and rubber. They're made of lots of molecules joined together...

Polymers are Long-Chain Molecules

1) Polymers are very large molecules.
2) Polymers are formed when lots of small molecules called monomers join together.
3) This reaction is called polymerisation — here's an example:

monomers

Pressure and Catalyst

polymer

This line shows that the molecule goes on and on...

4) There are different types of polymerisation reaction — the one above is an example of addition polymerisation. This is the only type you need to know about.
5) Alkene monomers join together in addition polymerisation (see p.42 for alkenes).
6) Polymerisation usually needs high pressure and a catalyst.

A catalyst is a chemical that speeds up a reaction without being used up.

Polymers are Named After the Monomers They're Made From

The name of the polymer comes from the type of monomer it's made from — you just stick the word "poly" in front of it:

Here's the reaction above again.

The monomers are called ethene...

Pressure and Catalyst

... so the polymer is called polyethene.

It's that simple. Here are a couple more examples:

Monomers

Chloroethene

Polymer

Polychloroethene

Monomers

Propene

Polymer

Polypropene

You can also work out the name of the monomer from the polymer name — just remove the poly.

Revision — it's all about stringing lots of facts together...

Which monomer a polymer is made from affects the properties of the plastic, which also affects what the plastic can be used for (more about the uses of plastics on the next page by the way). For this page, you need to be completely sure about what a monomer is, and how polymers are made.

Polymers and Their Uses

Plastics are a fantastically useful type of polymer. You can make novelty football pencil sharpeners and all sorts.

What Polymers Are Used For Depends On Their Properties

1) Different polymers have different properties — e.g. some are stronger and some are stretchier.

2) These different properties make them good for different uses.

- Polyethene is used for plastic bags because it's light and stretchable.
- Polystyrene foam is used in packaging to protect breakable things. It's also used to keep things hot because it's an insulator.
- Polyester is used to makes clothes. The polymers are strong which means clothes made from them last a long time.

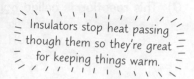

Insulators stop heat passing though them so they're great for keeping things warm.

Polymers are Often Used to Make Clothes

1) Nylon is a polymer that is often used to make clothes — especially outdoor clothing.

2) Nylon is easily coated to make it waterproof — so it keeps you dry in the wet.

3) It's also tough, lightweight and it can keep UV light out.

4) One big problem is that nylon clothing doesn't let water vapour pass through it. So if you get a bit hot (or do a bit of exercise), your sweat condenses on the inside. Eurrgh.

5) Some fabrics e.g. GORE-TEX® products, have all the useful properties of nylon, but are also breathable.

6) This means water vapour can escape — so there's no condensation and you don't get hot and sticky.

7) This material is great for outdoorsy types — they can hike without getting rained on or soaked in sweat.

Non-biodegradable Plastics Aren't Easy to Get Rid Of

1) Most polymers are non-biodegradable — they're not decomposed (broken down) by bacteria, so they don't rot.

2) This means that they're hard to get rid of.

3) We can get rid of waste plastics in different ways. For example:
- Burying them in landfill sites — but landfill sites fill up quickly, and they're a waste of land. And a waste of plastic.
- Burning them — but burning may release toxic gases that damage the environment. Plus it's a waste of plastic.
- Recycling them — this means the plastic is reused. But sorting out lots of different plastics for recycling is difficult and expensive.

4) Scientists are working on making polymers that biodegrade or dissolve. That way any plastic that is thrown away breaks down or dissolves rather than sitting there in landfill for ages.

Don't just leave it sitting there — break down and learn this page...

If you're making a product, you need to pick your plastic carefully. It's no good trying to make a kettle out of a plastic that melts at 50 °C when water boils at 100 °C — you'll end up with a messy kitchen, a burnt hand and no cuppa. You'd also have a bit of difficulty trying to wear clothes made of brittle, un-bendy plastic.

Hydrocarbons — Alkanes

Hydrocarbons might sound like fancy chemicals but really they're dead easy — just carbon and hydrogen.

Hydrocarbons Only Contain Hydrogen and Carbon Atoms

1) A hydrocarbon is any compound that is formed from carbon and hydrogen atoms only.

2) This means you can spot a hydrocarbon really easily by looking at its molecular or displayed formulas.

Molecular formula: $C_{10}H_{22}$ is a hydrocarbon — it's only made up of carbon (C) and hydrogen (H).
$CH_3COOC_3H_7$ is not a hydrocarbon — it's got oxygen (O) atoms in it.

Displayed formula:

This is a hydrocarbon. It has only C and H atoms.

This is not a hydrocarbon. It has an O atom.

Alkanes Are Hydrocarbons

1) Alkanes are the simplest type of hydrocarbon you can get.

2) They're just chains of carbon atoms joined together with hydrogen atoms attached around the outside.

3) All the carbons in an alkane are joined together by single covalent bonds.

This single line means it's a single bond.

4) The first four alkanes are methane (natural gas), ethane, propane and butane.

Methane: CH_4 Ethane: C_2H_6 Propane: C_3H_8 Butane: C_4H_{10}

(natural gas)

The 'a' bit of these names tells you the molecules are all alkanes.
It's really important that you spot them — you'll see why on the next page.

Alkane anybody who doesn't learn this lot properly...

For once scientists gave something a sensible name — hydrocarbons are molecules of hydrogen and carbon.
Make sure you learn what an alkane is — keep drawing out the structures of the examples on this page until you
get the hang of the basic pattern. They're important molecules in the modern world because they make good fuels.

Hydrocarbons — Alkenes

Don't confuse alkenes with alkanes — they have a different spelling, a different structure and different properties.

Alkenes Have Double Bonds

1) Alkenes are hydrocarbons too.

2) They are different to alkanes because they have double covalent bonds between some of the carbon atoms.

3) A double covalent bond means two pairs of electrons are shared (normally one pair is shared — see p. 30).

$$H_2C=CH_2$$

This double line means there's a double bond between these C atoms.

4) The first three alkenes are ethene, propene and butene:

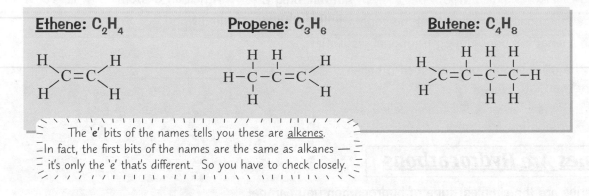

Ethene: C_2H_4   **Propene: C_3H_6**   **Butene: C_4H_8**

The 'e' bits of the names tells you these are alkenes. In fact, the first bits of the names are the same as alkanes — it's only the 'e' that's different. So you have to check closely.

Use Bromine Water as a Test For Alkenes

1) Bromine water is a bright orange solution that contains bromine (well, obviously).

2) It's really useful because it will react with double bonds.

3) When this happens the orange colour disappears from the solution — the bromine water is decolourised.

4) So, if you add an alkene to bromine water the colour will change from orange to colourless.

5) This means you can use bromine water to test if you've got an alkene.

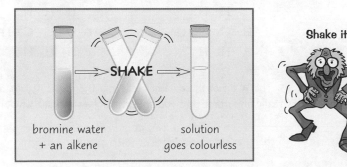

bromine water + an alkene   SHAKE   solution goes colourless

Shake it

The name's Bond Bond — Double Bond...

Just one double bond, that's all it takes to go from a boring alkane to a reactive alkene, able to make bromine water change colour. Amazing. Learn all of this page, including the displayed formulas, before moving on.

Fractional Distillation of Crude Oil

Fossil Fuels are a Finite Resource

1) <u>Coal</u>, <u>crude oil</u> and <u>gas</u> are all <u>fossil fuels</u>.

2) Fossil fuels are made from dead plants and animals that are buried for <u>millions of years</u>.

3) They're called <u>non-renewable</u> fuels. This is because they <u>take ages</u> to make and they're being <u>used up</u> much <u>faster</u> than they're being <u>made</u>.

4) Fossil fuels are <u>finite</u> resources (there's a limited amount) because they are <u>no longer being made</u> or are being made <u>very slowly</u>. So one day they'll <u>run out</u>.

Crude Oil is Separated into Different Hydrocarbon Fractions

1) <u>Crude oil</u> is a <u>mixture</u> of lots of <u>different hydrocarbons</u>.

2) The substances in crude oil can be <u>separated</u> by a process called <u>fractional distillation</u>.

3) Here's what happens during fractional distillation.

- The oil is <u>heated</u> until most of it has turned into <u>gas</u>.
- The gases enter a tall tower called a <u>fractionating column</u>.
- In the column it's <u>hot</u> at the <u>bottom</u> and gets gradually <u>cooler</u> as you go up — this is called a <u>temperature gradient</u>.
- Hydrocarbons with <u>high boiling points</u> leave the column near the <u>bottom</u>. (These are the <u>largest molecules</u>.)
- Hydrocarbons with <u>lower boiling points</u> leave the column near to the <u>top</u>. (These are <u>smallest molecules</u>.)

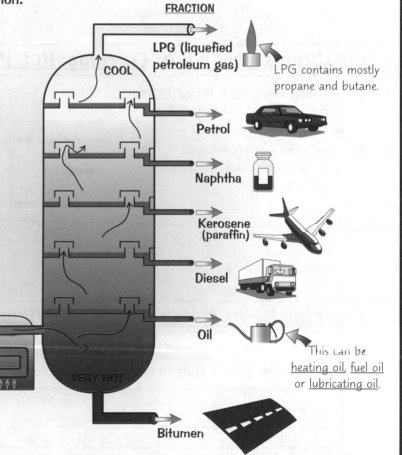

FRACTION

LPG (liquefied petroleum gas) — LPG contains mostly propane and butane.

Petrol

Naphtha

Kerosene (paraffin)

Diesel

Oil — This can be <u>heating oil</u>, <u>fuel oil</u> or <u>lubricating oil</u>.

Crude oil

COOL

VERY HOT

Bitumen

4) You end up with the crude oil mixture separated out into <u>groups of hydrocarbons</u>.

5) These groups are called <u>fractions</u>.

6) Each fraction contains a <u>mixture</u> of hydrocarbons with <u>similar boiling points</u>.

7) The separated fractions are much <u>more useful</u> than crude oil.

How much petrol is there in crude oil? Just a fraction...

In the exam, you could be given a diagram of the fractional distillation column and asked to add labels, or say where on the column a certain fraction (like petrol or diesel) would drain off. This means you need to learn the diagram properly — don't just glance at it and <u>think</u> you know it. <u>Cover the page up</u> and <u>test yourself</u>.

Cracking

Crude oil fractions from fractional distillation can be split into smaller molecules — this is called cracking. It's dead important — otherwise we might not have enough fuel for cars and planes and things.

Cracking is Splitting Up Long-Chain Hydrocarbons

1) Cracking turns long alkane molecules into smaller alkane and alkene molecules. For example:

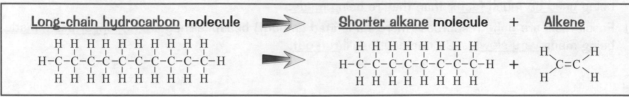

Long-chain hydrocarbon molecule ⟹ Shorter alkane molecule + Alkene

2) Smaller alkanes and alkenes are much more useful than longer alkanes.
3) The alkene molecules made by cracking can be used to make polymers (mostly plastics).
4) Cracking is also a useful way to make more petrol.

Conditions Needed for Cracking: Hot, Plus a Catalyst

1) Cracking needs high temperatures and a catalyst (a chemical that speeds up the reaction).
2) Here's the equipment you need to crack the hydrocarbon paraffin in the lab:

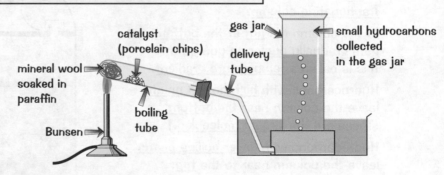

Cracking Helps Match Supply and Demand

1) Supply is how much of a substance there is. Demand is how much of a substance people want.
2) You might be given a table to show the supply and demand for different crude oil fractions.

Fraction	Supply (approx % in crude oil)	Demand (approx % demand)
LPG	2	4
Petrol and naphtha	16	27
Kerosene	13	8
Diesel	19	23
Oil and bitumen	50	38

There is more demand for petrol and naphtha than supply.

There is more supply of kerosene than demand. The kerosene can be cracked to make the extra petrol that's needed.

Don't crack up, it's not that bad...

Cracking helps an oil refinery to match its supply of useful products, like petrol, with the demand for them. It also produces short chain alkenes that can be used to make plastics. Remember, you can crack any long hydrocarbon chain into smaller chains, but you can't make longer chains from shorter ones by cracking.

Use of Fossil Fuels

Nothing as amazingly useful as crude oil would be without its problems. No, that'd be too good to be true.

Oil is Very Useful Stuff, but It Can Cause Big Problems Too

1) Crude oil is found in the Earth's crust.
2) To get it out holes need to be drilled so the oil can be pumped to the surface.
3) It can then be transported to where it's needed.
4) Most of the problems with crude oil happen when it's being transported from one place to another.

- If a ship carrying oil crashes the crude oil may escape.
  The oil will then float on water and spread out into big oil slicks.
- The oil may cover sea birds' feathers and stop them being waterproof.
  Water then soaks into their downy feathers, and they can die of cold.
- If birds swallow the oil as they try to clean themselves, they may get poisoned and this could kill them too.
- Also, birds can't fly when their feathers are matted with oil.
- If the slick comes ashore, beaches might become covered in oil.
- Chemicals called detergents are used to try and clean up oil slicks, but these can harm wildlife too.

There's Lots to Think About When Choosing the Best Fuel

There are lots of different fuels and lots of things to think about when choosing the best one. For example:
1) Energy value — the amount of energy the fuel gives out.
2) Availability — there's not much point in choosing a fuel you can't get hold of easily.
3) Storage — some fuels take up a lot of space.
4) Cost — some fuels are more expensive than others.
5) Toxicity — some fuels are toxic and produce poisonous gases when they burn.
6) Ease of use — whether it lights easily, whether you can move it safely.
7) Pollution — e.g. will it cause acid rain or increase the greenhouse effect.

Example: You're at home and there's a power cut. You want a cup of tea. The only fuels you have in the house are candles or meths (in a spirit burner). Which one would you use to boil the water?

Fuel	Energy per gram	Rate of energy produced	Flame
Meths	28 kJ	15 kJ per minute	Clean
Candle	50 kJ	8 kJ per minute	Smoky

Even though a candle has more energy per gram, you'd probably choose meths because it's quicker and cleaner.

Oil not be impressed if you don't bother learning this...

Erk, what a page. Right, the best thing to do is divide it into chunks and learn it that way. Start with where the oil comes from. Then do the effects of oil slicks on wildlife, learn it and get it sorted. Then learn the factors involved with choosing a fuel, and run through the example so you're absolutely sure.

Burning Fuels

Combust baby combust, disco inferno — combustion is just the fancy word for burning.

Complete Combustion Happens When There's Plenty of Oxygen

1) The combustion of a fuel needs oxygen.
2) When there's plenty of oxygen, this reaction is known as complete combustion.
3) It releases lots of useful heat energy.
4) The complete combustion of a hydrocarbon only produces carbon dioxide and water.

> hydrocarbon + oxygen ⟶ carbon dioxide + water   (+ energy)

5) A Bunsen burner will burn with a clean blue flame when combustion is complete.
6) You can do an experiment to show that you get CO₂ and H₂O when you burn a hydrocarbon.

- The water pump draws gases from the burning hydrocarbon through the equipment.
- Water collects inside the U-tube.
- You can show that it's water by checking its boiling point — it should be 100 °C.
- The limewater turns milky, showing that carbon dioxide is present.

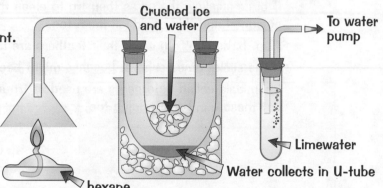

Cruched ice and water
To water pump
Limewater
Water collects in U-tube
hexane

Incomplete Combustion of Hydrocarbons is NOT Safe

1) If there isn't enough oxygen when you burn a fuel, combustion will be incomplete.
2) The fuel will burn with a yellow flame.
3) This produces carbon monoxide, carbon (soot) and water.

> hydrocarbon + oxygen ⟶ carbon monoxide + water + carbon   (+ energy)

4) Carbon monoxide is a poisonous gas and it's very dangerous.
5) Incomplete combustion releases less energy than complete combustion.
6) So basically, you want lots of oxygen when you're burning fuel, because:
- you get more heat energy given out,
- you don't get any messy soot,
- you don't get any poisonous gases.

Where did I get that video of collecting water — U-tube...

In the exam you might get asked to write out a word equation for the combustion of a certain fuel, for example, methane. All you need to do is replace hydrocarbon in the word equations above with the name of the fuel you're given. So, the answer for this example would be: methane + oxygen → carbon dioxide + water.

Module C1 — Carbon Chemistry

The Atmosphere

The atmosphere is all the air between the ground and space. It's made up of different gases. You need to know how it was made and how it's changed.

The Atmosphere Has Changed

How it started

1) The Earth's early atmosphere was made from gases that escaped from inside the Earth when volcanoes erupted.

2) The early atmosphere was probably made up of mostly carbon dioxide and steam.

How it is now

1) After a few billion years green plants started to grow.

2) The green plants removed carbon dioxide from the air for photosynthesis.

3) The plants also produced oxygen by photosynthesis.

4) So photosynthesis reduced the amount of carbon dioxide in the air and increased the amount of oxygen until they reached the levels they're at today.

5) Combustion (burning) and respiration (a chemical reaction done by animals) do the opposite.

6) They increase the amount of carbon dioxide and reduce the amount of oxygen in the air.

Today's Atmosphere is Just Right for Us

Today, the atmosphere is mostly made up from nitrogen, oxygen and carbon dioxide:

78% nitrogen
21% oxygen
0.035% carbon dioxide

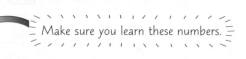

Make sure you learn these numbers.

There is also some water vapour in the atmosphere.

The amount of nitrogen, oxygen and carbon dioxide in the air today pretty much stays the same.

4 billion years ago, it was a whole other world...

Sometimes people talk about how the present day atmosphere has evolved — evolved is just a scientific word for changing over time. And it's amazing how much the atmosphere of Planet Earth has actually changed.

The Carbon Cycle

Carbon seems to be in almost everything — the air, plants, animals, fossil fuels, the T-shirt you're wearing and the piece of toast you had for breakfast. But it doesn't just stay in one place, it moves around between all these things in the <u>carbon cycle</u>...

Carbon is Constantly Being Recycled

The carbon on Earth moves in a <u>big cycle</u> — the diagram below is a pretty good summary.

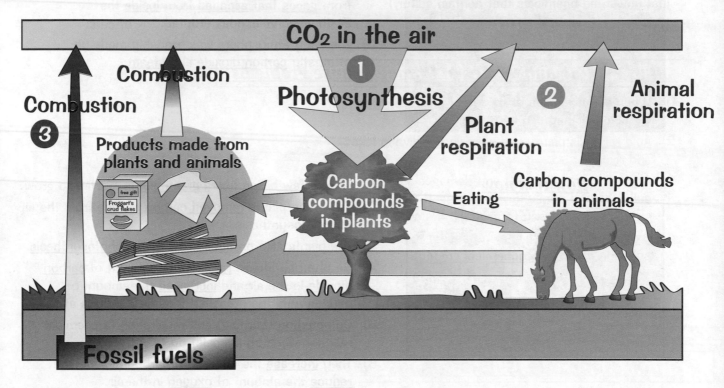

This diagram isn't as big and scary as it might look. The important things you need to remember are:

1 <u>Photosynthesis</u> by plants <u>removes</u> carbon dioxide from the <u>air</u>.

2 <u>Respiration</u> by plants and animals <u>adds</u> carbon dioxide to the <u>air</u>.

3 <u>Combustion</u> (burning) of fuels and products <u>adds</u> carbon dioxide to the <u>air</u>.

Eeeek — the carbon cycle's got a puncture...

The <u>carbon cycle</u> is a cycle so you can start learning it anywhere you like. <u>Photosynthesis</u> is as good a place as any. Then you just need to add <u>respiration</u> on one side and <u>combustion</u> on the other. Just make sure you get the arrows in the right direction. Have a couple of goes, you'll soon get it.

Air Pollution and Acid Rain

Carbon dioxide is released into the air when fossil fuels burn but it's not the only gas —
you also get other nasties like <u>oxides of nitrogen</u>, <u>sulfur dioxide</u> and <u>carbon monoxide</u>.

Burning Fossil Fuels Releases Sulfur Dioxide and Oxides of Nitrogen

1) When <u>fossil fuels</u> are burned harmful gases are released, e.g. <u>sulfur dioxide</u> and <u>nitrogen oxides</u>.

2) The <u>sulfur dioxide</u> (SO_2) comes from <u>sulfur impurities</u> in the <u>fossil fuels</u>. (Sulfur impurities are just unwanted chemicals that contain sulfur.)

3) The <u>nitrogen oxides</u> are made when fuels are burnt in the internal combustion <u>engines</u> of cars.

Sulfur Dioxide and Oxides of Nitrogen Cause Problems

1) When sulfur dioxide or oxides of nitrogen <u>mix</u> with <u>clouds</u> they can cause <u>acid rain</u>.

2) <u>Acid rain</u> kills plants and animals that live in lakes and rivers.

3) Acid rain also kills <u>trees</u> and damages <u>limestone</u> buildings and ruins <u>stone statues</u>. It also causes <u>metals</u> to wear away (corrode). It's shocking.

4) <u>Oxides of nitrogen</u> can also cause a type of air pollution called <u>photochemical smog</u>.

Carbon Monoxide is a Poisonous Gas

1) <u>Carbon monoxide</u> (CO) is a <u>poisonous gas</u>.

2) Carbon monoxide is formed when <u>petrol or diesel</u> in car engines is burnt without enough oxygen — this is <u>incomplete combustion</u> (see page 46 for more details).

It's Important That Air Pollution is Controlled

1) The build-up of all these pollutants can make life <u>unhealthy and miserable</u> for many people.

2) For example, there are a lot more people with breathing illnesses like <u>asthma</u> now.

3) Many people blame air pollution for this.

4) There are things that can be done to <u>control</u> air pollution.

5) For example, having <u>catalytic converters</u> in motor vehicles reduces the amount of <u>carbon monoxide</u> coming out of the exhausts. They do this by converting it to <u>carbon dioxide</u>.

Revision and pollution — the two problems with modern life...

Eeee... <u>cars</u> and <u>fossil fuels</u> — they're nothing but trouble. But at least this topic is kind of interesting, what with its relevance to <u>everyday life</u> and all. Just think... you could see this kind of stuff on TV.

Revision Summary for Module C1

Okay, if you were just about to turn the page without doing these revision summary questions, then stop. What kind of an attitude is that... Is that really the way you want to live your life... running, playing and having fun... Of course not. That's right. Do the questions. It's for the best all round.

1) What is the name for a substance that contains more than one type of atom?

2) Name two types of chemical bond.

3) A molecule has the molecular formula $CH_3CH_2CH_3$. How many H and C atoms does it contain?

4) Write down the displayed formula for a molecule with the formula CH_4.

5) Name the reactants and the products in this reaction:
methane + oxygen → carbon dioxide + water

6) Balance this equation which shows the combustion of methane: $CH_4 + O_2 \rightarrow CO_2 + H_2O$.

7) What does an emulsifier do to oil and water?

8) Complete the word equation for the decomposition of baking powder
sodium hydrogencarbonate → sodium carbonate + ... + ...

9) What substances react to make an ester and water?

10) Give three properties that a substance must have in order to make a good perfume.

11) In salt water, what is: a) the solute,   b) the solution?

12) What is the solvent in emulsion paint?

13) What are thermochromic pigments? Give four uses for them.

14) Name the polymer that's made from the monomer ethene.

15) Give two properties of nylon that make it good for outdoor clothing.

16) What are the two types of atom in a hydrocarbon?

17) What is the difference between an alkane and an alkene?

18) True or false: in a fractionating column hydrocarbons with the lowest boiling points leave the column at the bottom.

19) What is cracking used for?

20) What two conditions are needed for cracking to happen?

21) How might an oil slick harm sea birds?

22) Give four things that affect what fuel you would choose for a particular job.

23) Give two advantages of complete combustion over incomplete combustion.

24) Write down the word equation for the complete combustion of ethane.

25) 3 billion years ago, the Earth's atmosphere was mostly CO_2. Where did this CO_2 come from?

26) Today, there's mostly O_2 and N_2 in the Earth's atmosphere. What process produced the O_2?

27) Draw and label a diagram of the carbon cycle.

28) Name a poisonous gas that catalytic converters help to remove from car exhausts.

Heat

When it starts to get a bit cold, on goes the heating to warm things up a bit.
Heating is all about the <u>transfer of energy</u>.

Heat is a Measure of Energy

1) When a substance is <u>heated</u>, its particles gain <u>energy</u>.

2) This energy makes the particles in a <u>gas or a liquid</u> move around <u>faster</u>.

3) In a solid, the particles <u>vibrate (shake) faster</u>.

4) Heat energy is measured in <u>joules (J)</u>.

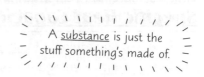

A <u>substance</u> is just the stuff something's made of.

Temperature is a Measure of Hotness

1) The <u>hotter</u> something is, the <u>higher its temperature</u>.

2) The <u>colder</u> something is, the <u>lower its temperature</u>.

3) Temperature is <u>measured</u> in <u>°C</u> (degrees Celsius).

4) If two things have <u>DIFFERENT TEMPERATURES</u>, HEAT <u>ENERGY WILL FLOW</u> between them.

5) <u>Energy</u> will <u>flow</u> from <u>hot objects</u> to <u>cooler</u> ones.

6) This makes the hot objects <u>cool down</u> until they're at the <u>same temperature</u> as the <u>air in the room</u>.

7) And it makes <u>cold</u> objects <u>warm up</u> until they reach <u>room temperature</u>.

8) <u>Warm radiators</u> heat the <u>cold air</u> in your room — they'd be <u>no use</u> if heat didn't <u>flow</u>.

9) The <u>rate of cooling</u> (how <u>quickly</u> something cools down) depends on the <u>difference</u> in temperature between a hot <u>object</u> and its <u>surroundings</u> (where it is).

10) For example, a <u>hot</u> mug of tea will cool down <u>faster</u> in a <u>cold</u> room than in a <u>warm</u> room.

11) The <u>HOTTER</u> an object is compared with its surroundings, the <u>QUICKER</u> it loses heat.

Hot cup of coffee gets <u>cooler</u>

Energy   Energy   Energy   Energy

Cold air gets <u>warmer</u>

Thermograms Show Temperatures

1) A <u>thermogram</u> is a picture taken with a <u>special camera</u> that <u>detects heat</u>.

2) <u>Different temperatures</u> show up as a range of <u>different colours</u>.

3) The <u>hotter</u> parts show up as <u>white</u>, <u>yellow</u> and <u>red</u>.

4) The <u>colder</u> parts are <u>black</u>, <u>dark blue</u> and <u>purple</u>.

5) In this thermogram, the <u>roofs</u> of the houses on the <u>left and right</u> are <u>red</u> so they are at a <u>higher temperature</u> than the <u>blue</u> roof of the house <u>in between</u>.

6) That's because they're <u>losing heat</u> to the outside from their <u>roofs</u>.

© TONY MCCONNELL/
SCIENCE PHOTO LIBRARY

I went to a physicist's stag night — the best man had booked a thermogram...

It makes sense — <u>hot</u> things <u>cool down</u>, and <u>cold</u> things <u>warm up</u>, until they reach room temperature.
Make sure you learn all the points about temperature and energy, including what they're both <u>measured</u> in.

Specific Heat Capacity

Don't be put off by the scary sounding name. <u>Specific heat capacity</u> just tells you <u>how much heat energy</u> something needs to make its <u>temperature rise</u>.

Specific Heat Capacity Tells You How Much Energy Stuff Can Store

1) To make something's <u>temperature rise</u>, you need to give it <u>energy</u>.

2) The <u>amount</u> of energy it needs depends on <u>three things</u>:
   - Its <u>mass</u> (how much of it there is).
   - What it's <u>made of</u>.
   - <u>How much</u> you want the <u>temperature</u> to rise (the <u>temperature change</u>).

3) It takes <u>more</u> heat energy to increase the temperature of <u>some materials</u> than others. For example, it takes more energy to heat some <u>water</u> by <u>1 °C</u> than for the same amount of <u>mercury</u>.

4) Materials which need <u>lots of energy</u> to <u>warm up</u> store a lot of heat.

5) <u>How much energy</u> a substance can <u>store</u> is called its <u>specific heat capacity</u> (SHC).

6) <u>SPECIFIC HEAT CAPACITY</u> is the amount of <u>ENERGY</u> needed to raise the temperature of <u>1 kg</u> of a substance by <u>1 °C</u>.

You Can Measure the SHC Of Substances

1) To find the <u>specific heat capacity</u> of something you have to measure:
   - the amount of <u>heat energy</u> added
   - the <u>temperature change</u>

2) Set up the <u>equipment</u> like in the diagram on the right.

3) The <u>heating coil</u> gives <u>heat energy</u> to the water which <u>increases its temperature</u>.

4) Measure the temperature <u>change</u> with the <u>thermometer</u>.

5) The amount of <u>heat</u> added can be worked out from the <u>voltage</u> and <u>current</u> of the heater <u>AND</u> the <u>time</u> it's turned on for.
   (You don't need to know how to do that though.)

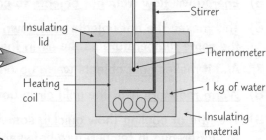

Energy = Mass x SHC x Temperature Change

1) You'll have to do <u>calculations</u> involving <u>specific heat capacity</u>.

2) This is the <u>formula</u> to learn:

Energy = Mass × Specific Heat Capacity × Temperature Change
(J)   (kg)   (J/kg°C)   (°C)

EXAMPLE: How much energy is needed to heat 2 kg of water from 10 °C to 100 °C? The SHC of water is 4200 J/kg°C.

ANSWER: Temperature change = 100 °C − 10 °C = <u>90 °C</u>.
Energy = Mass × SHC × Temp Change
So energy needed = 2 kg × 4200 J/kg°C × 90 °C = <u>756 000 J</u>

I wish I had a high specific fact capacity...

There are <u>two reasons</u> why water's used in central heating systems. It's a <u>liquid</u> so it can be easily pumped around, and it also has a <u>high specific heat capacity</u> so it can store and give out loads of heat. This makes water good for <u>cooling systems</u> too — it can <u>absorb</u> a lot of energy and <u>carry it away</u>.

Melting and Boiling

If you heat up a pan of water, the water never gets any hotter than 100 °C. You can <u>carry on heating it</u>, but the <u>temperature won't rise</u>. Why? It's all to do with <u>latent heat</u>.

You Need to Put in Energy to Melt or Boil Something

1) When you heat a solid, the <u>temperature goes up</u> until you reach the <u>melting point</u> (see ① on graph).

2) At the melting point ②, the temperature <u>stops increasing</u> until <u>all the solid</u> has <u>changed state</u> into a <u>liquid</u>.

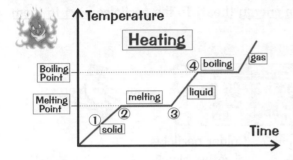

3) The temperature of the liquid then starts <u>increasing again</u> at ③ until you reach the <u>boiling point</u>.

4) At the boiling point ④, the temperature doesn't increase until <u>all the liquid</u> has <u>changed state</u> again into <u>gas</u>.

5) All the energy you're <u>adding</u> is being used to <u>change the state</u>, instead of increasing the temperature.

6) The <u>flat bits</u> on the graph show where this happens.

Energy is Given Out During Freezing

1) Energy is <u>given out</u> when a gas <u>changes</u> to a liquid (<u>condensing</u>), or a liquid changes to a solid (<u>freezing</u>).

2) When this is happening, the temperature <u>stays the same</u>.

3) The <u>flat bits</u> on the graph here show this too.

4) The <u>temperature doesn't go down</u> until all the substance has <u>changed state</u>.

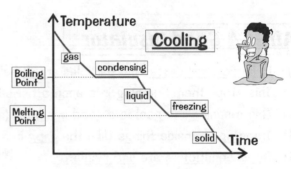

Specific Latent Heat is the Energy Needed to Change State

1) <u>Specific latent heat</u> (<u>SLH</u>) of a material is the amount of <u>energy</u> needed for it to <u>change state</u>.

2) Specific latent heat is <u>different</u> for <u>different materials</u>.

3) It's also different for <u>boiling</u> and <u>melting</u>.

4) The <u>SPECIFIC LATENT HEAT OF MELTING</u> is the <u>amount of energy</u> needed to <u>MELT 1 kg</u> of material <u>without changing its temperature</u>.

5) The <u>SPECIFIC LATENT HEAT OF BOILING</u> is the <u>energy</u> needed to <u>BOIL 1 kg</u> of material <u>without changing its temperature</u>.

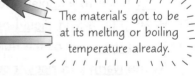

The material's got to be at its melting or boiling temperature already.

6) Use this formula to do <u>SLH calculations</u> in the exam:

$$\text{Energy} = \text{Mass} \times \text{Specific Latent Heat}$$
$$\text{(J)} \qquad \text{(kg)} \qquad \text{(J/kg)}$$

<u>EXAMPLE:</u> The specific latent heat of water (for melting) is 334 000 J/kg. How much energy is needed to melt an ice cube of mass 0.007 kg at 0 °C?

<u>ANSWER:</u> Energy = Mass × SLH = 0.007 kg × 334 000 J/kg = <u>2338 J</u>

Can't stand the heat — melt...
<u>Changing state</u> takes <u>energy</u>. Specific latent heat is just the <u>amount</u> of energy you need to put in to do it.

Conduction and Convection in the Home

Houses lose a lot of heat through their windows and walls by conduction.
But it's convection that lets you feel the heat from a radiator on the other side of the room.

Conduction Happens Mainly in Solids

1) In a solid, the particles are held tightly together.
2) So when one particle vibrates (shakes), it bumps into other particles nearby.
3) HEAT CONDUCTION is where vibrating particles pass on extra energy (heat) to the particles next to them.
4) This makes the heat spread all the way through the solid.

Hotter particles
vibrating faster

Vibrations and heat
energy get passed on

Colder particles
vibrating slowly

Air Is A Good Insulator

1) In liquids and gases, the particles aren't held so tightly together.
2) This stops them bumping into each other as often, so they conduct heat more slowly than solids.
3) This means air (a gas) is a good insulator (something which doesn't conduct heat very well).
4) Trapping air inside things (like the gaps in a woolly jumper) makes them better at insulating.
5) Good conductors are bad insulators.
6) Metals are good conductors of heat.
   For example, a metal spoon in a hot drink will get hot quickly, as will a metal saucepan.

Convection Happens in Liquids and Gases

1) CONVECTION is where particles with more energy move from a hot place to a cooler one taking their heat energy with them.
2) Heating up a fluid (liquid or gas) gives the particles more energy so they move around faster.
3) The warmer part of the fluid rises above the colder parts.
4) As the warm part rises, cooler fluid falls and takes its place.
5) This carries on so you have a circular flow of fluid — called a convection current.
6) This is how radiators spread warm air around the room.
7) Convection can't happen in solids because the particles can't move.
8) To stop convection, you need to stop the liquid or gas moving.
   For example: clothes, blankets and wall insulation all work by trapping pockets of air which can't move.

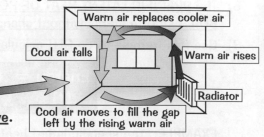

Warm air replaces cooler air

Cool air falls

Warm air rises

Radiator

Cool air moves to fill the gap
left by the rising warm air

And the good old garden spade is a great example...

If a garden spade is left outside in cold weather, the metal bit will always feel colder than the wooden handle.
But it isn't colder — metal just conducts heat away from your hand quicker than wood so it makes it feel colder.

Heat Radiation

Houses in hot countries are often painted white, to reflect heat from the Sun.
In cold, cloudy Britain, we tend to leave our houses grey or red to absorb the heat. (Saves on paint, too.)

All Objects Emit and Absorb Heat Radiation

1) Heat is radiated (given out) as infrared radiation (see p. 62).
2) You can feel this heat radiation.
   For example, you feel warm when the Sun shines on you.
3) Objects can emit (give out) and absorb (take in) heat radiation.
4) The hotter an object is, the more heat radiation it emits.
5) Cooler objects will absorb the heat radiation emitted by hotter objects around them.
6) When something absorbs heat radiation, its temperature rises.

Colour And Texture Affect How Much Heat Is Absorbed

1) Matt (dull), rough and black surfaces are very good at absorbing and emitting heat radiation.
2) So you should really paint your radiators black to help them emit heat radiation.
3) White or light-coloured, and smooth surfaces are very bad at absorbing and emitting heat radiation.
4) So you should leave your fridge white to help keep heat away from the food inside.
5) Shiny surfaces reflect heat radiation — so they don't absorb it either.
6) Putting shiny foil behind radiators reflects heat back into the room, rather than heating up the walls.

Examples:

The shiny surface on a patio heater reflects heat downwards — onto the patio.

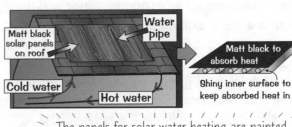

The panels for solar water heating are painted matt black to absorb as much heat as possible.

Heat Radiation is Important in Cooking

1) Grills and toasters heat food using infrared radiation.
2) The heat radiated by a grill is absorbed by the surface particles of the food.
3) The heat energy is then conducted or convected to the middle parts.
4) People often line their grill pan with shiny foil.
5) This reflects the heat back onto the bottom of the food being grilled to cook it more evenly.

See the previous page for more on conduction and convection.

Radiate happiness — stand by the fire and smile...

The confusing thing about radiation is that the 'radiators' on your wall at home actually heat the room by convection. They should probably have been called 'convectors'. Learn this page, then go make me some toast.

Saving Energy

It'd be daft to keep buying hamsters and letting them all escape.
It's also daft to keep paying for energy to heat your house, only to let the heat escape straight out again.

Insulating Your House Saves Energy and Money

Insulate means doing stuff to stop heat escaping.

1) Things that emit (give out) energy are called sources, e.g. radiators.
2) Things that use and waste or lose energy are called sinks, e.g. windows and computers.
3) To save energy, you can insulate your house so less energy is lost through the sinks.
4) You can also save energy by buying sources and sinks that are more efficient
   — they're better at their job so they use and waste less energy.
5) Insulation and efficient sources and sinks can cost a lot to buy but using them makes energy bills lower.
6) After a while, the money you've saved on energy bills will equal the initial cost of buying them.
7) The time this takes is called the payback time.

Payback time = initial cost ÷ annual saving

Annual saving is how much you save on bills each year.

8) The shorter the payback time, the more cost-effective
   something is (see below for examples).

Most Insulation Traps Air

1) To stop heat being lost, you need to reduce conduction, convection and radiation.
2) Putting shiny foil behind wall heaters can reduce heat loss by radiation by reflecting heat back.
3) Conduction and convection can usually be reduced by trapping air.
4) This is because air is a good insulator and poor conductor (see page 54).
5) Here are some examples of how to save energy in the home that you need to learn:

Loft Insulation

A thick layer of fibreglass wool laid across the loft floor and ceiling
reduces heat loss from the house by conduction and convection.
It also traps air which is a good insulator.
Initial Cost: £200 Annual Saving: £100
Payback time: 200 ÷ 100 = 2 years

The figures used here are rough. It'll vary from house to house.

Double Glazing

Two layers of glass with an air gap
between them reduces conduction.
Initial Cost: £2400
Annual Saving: £80
Payback time: 30 years

Cavity Walls & Insulation

Two layers of bricks with a gap
between them reduce conduction.
Insulating foam or fibreglass is added
into the gap between layers, trapping
pockets of air to reduce convection.
Initial Cost: £150
Annual Saving: £100
Payback time: 18 months

Draught-proofing

Strips of foam and plastic around
doors and windows stop hot air
going out — reducing convection.

Thick Curtains

Reduce the amount of radiation
passing through the windows. They
also trap air between them and the
window which reduces conduction.

Or you could just wear an extra jumper...

Insulating your house well is a really good way to save energy. Drawing the curtains is like putting on
another jumper. Except people can still stare nosily at you when you've put your jumper on.

Efficiency

An open fire looks cosy, but a lot of its heat energy goes straight up the chimney by <u>convection</u>, instead of heating up your living room. All this energy is '<u>wasted</u>', so open fires aren't very <u>efficient</u>.

Machines Always Waste Some Energy

1) Machines <u>change energy</u> from <u>one form</u> to <u>another</u>.
   For example, you put <u>chemical energy</u> into a car (petrol or diesel) and the engine converts it into <u>kinetic (movement) energy</u>.

2) The <u>total energy out</u> is always the <u>same</u> as the <u>total energy put in</u> — energy is always <u>conserved</u>.

3) But only some of the energy that comes out is <u>useful</u>.

4) The rest of the <u>energy</u> is <u>wasted</u>, often as <u>heat</u>.
   In the car example, a lot of the chemical energy is changed into wasted <u>heat and sound energy</u>.

<u>Conserved</u> means the amount <u>stays the same</u>.

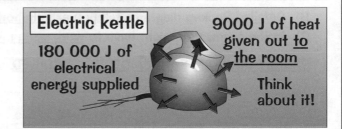

More Efficient Machines Waste Less Energy

You can <u>calculate</u> the <u>efficiency</u> of a machine using this equation:

$$\text{Efficiency} = \frac{\text{USEFUL Energy OUTPUT}}{\text{TOTAL Energy INPUT}} \ (\times \ 100\%)$$

<u>EXAMPLE:</u> A kettle uses 180 000 J to boil some water. 9000 J is wasted in heating up the air around the kettle. What is the kettle's efficiency?

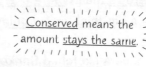
Electric kettle
180 000 J of electrical energy supplied
9000 J of heat given out <u>to</u> the room
Think about it!

<u>ANSWER:</u>

1) First find out the <u>Total Energy IN</u>.
   In this case it's <u>180 000 J</u>.

2) Then find the <u>Useful Energy OUT</u>.

3) The question might give you this, or it might tell you how much energy is <u>wasted</u>.

4) <u>Useful Energy = Total Energy − Wasted Energy</u>.
   Useful Energy in the kettle = 180 000 J − 9000 J = <u>171 000 J</u>.

5) Next, <u>divide</u> the <u>smaller number</u> (useful) by the <u>bigger one</u> (total) to get an <u>efficiency</u>.

6) You should get an answer somewhere between <u>0 and 1</u>.

7) If your number is bigger than 1, you've done the division <u>upside down</u>.
   <u>Efficiency</u> of the kettle = Useful ÷ Total = Small ÷ Big = 171 000 ÷ 180 000 = <u>0.95</u>.

8) You can change your answer to a <u>percentage</u> by multiplying it by 100.
   Efficiency = 0.95 × 100 = <u>95%</u>.

9) You can use the formula with <u>Sankey diagrams</u> too — coming up on the next page.

Efficiency = pages learned ÷ cups of tea made...

Some machines, like fridges, are given a letter A to H, to show how <u>efficient</u> they are. A really <u>efficient fridge</u> might be given an 'A'. But if you put it near the oven, or don't defrost it, it will waste more energy than it should.

Sankey Diagrams

This is another opportunity for a **MATHS** question. Great. Here's what Sankey diagrams are all about.

The Thickness of the Arrow Shows the Amount of Energy

1) Sankey diagrams are energy transformation diagrams.
2) They show how much of the energy put in is changed into useful energy and how much is wasted energy.
3) But remember that the total amount of energy stays the same because it's conserved (see page 57).
4) This means total energy in = total energy out.
5) Thicker arrows mean more energy.
6) You have a big thick arrow going in, then thinner arrows going off it.
7) You can have a sketched Sankey diagram.
8) You don't know the actual amount of energy, but the thickest arrows show the most energy.
9) In this example, the biggest arrow is for the waste heat, so most of the energy is being wasted.
10) In the exam, you might have to look at two sketches for different things and say which is more efficient.
11) Look for the one with the thickest useful energy arrow(s).

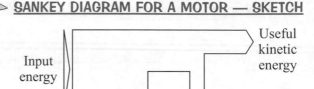

In a motor, heat and sound is wasted energy.

SANKEY DIAGRAM FOR A MOTOR — SKETCH

Input energy — Useful kinetic energy — Heat energy — Sound energy

You Could Be Given a Detailed Sankey Diagram

1) Detailed Sankey diagrams tell you exactly how much energy goes in, is wasted, and is useful.
2) In the exam, you might have to work out a missing value on a Sankey diagram.

SANKEY DIAGRAM FOR A MOTOR — DETAILED

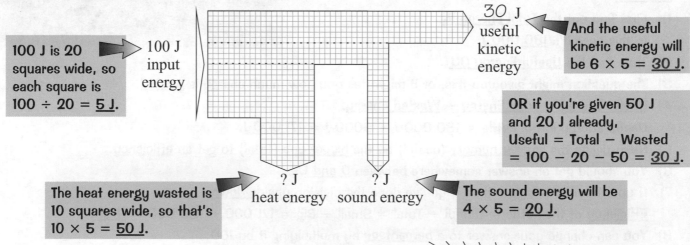

100 J is 20 squares wide, so each square is 100 ÷ 20 = **5 J**.

100 J input energy

30 J useful kinetic energy

And the useful kinetic energy will be 6 × 5 = **30 J**.

OR if you're given 50 J and 20 J already, Useful = Total − Wasted = 100 − 20 − 50 = **30 J**.

The heat energy wasted is 10 squares wide, so that's 10 × 5 = **50 J**.

? J heat energy — ? J sound energy

The sound energy will be 4 × 5 = **20 J**.

You could also be asked to work out the efficiency from a Sankey diagram (see p. 57). For example, from this diagram:

Efficiency = Useful ÷ Total (× 100) = 30 J ÷ 100 J (× 100)
= 0.3 (× 100) = **30%**.

Sankey diagrams show energy being conserved: total input = useful energy + wasted energy.

Skankey diagrams — to show the smelliness of your socks...

Most things waste lots of energy, usually as heat. This means they'll have a thick 'waste' arrow. You need the useful energy to calculate the efficiency, so make sure you learn how to find it from the diagram.

Wave Basics

Waves crop up all over the place. They're used for communication, in medicine, and even for cooking. To start us off, here's some general stuff on waves.

Waves Have Amplitude, Wavelength and Frequency

1) The amplitude is the distance from the rest position to a crest OR trough (NOT from a trough to a crest).

2) The wavelength is the length of a full cycle of the wave. For example, from crest to crest.

3) Frequency is the number of complete waves passing a certain point per second.

4) Frequency is measured in hertz (Hz).

5) 1 Hz is 1 wave per second.

6) All electromagnetic waves (see p. 62) travel at the same high speed in a vacuum (like in space).

7) This is known as 'the speed of light' and is 300 000 000 m/s.

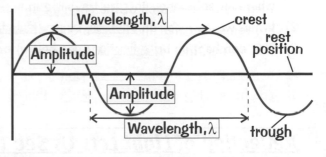

A vacuum has nothing in it, not even air.

Wave Speed = Frequency x Wavelength

1) You need to be able to use this equation:

$$\text{Speed} = \text{Frequency} \times \text{Wavelength}$$
$$\text{(m/s)} \quad \text{(Hz)} \quad \text{(m)}$$

OR 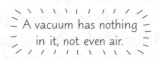 $v = f\lambda$

Speed (v is for velocity)

Frequency

Wavelength (that's the Greek letter 'lambda')

EXAMPLE: Calculate the speed of a wave with frequency 0.5 Hz and wavelength 0.9 m.

ANSWER: Speed = frequency × wavelength = 0.5 × 0.90 = 0.45 m/s.

2) The units you need for the wave equation are: metres, m/s and hertz (Hz).

3) Always CONVERT (CHANGE) INTO THESE UNITS before you work anything out.

4) Waves often have high frequencies given in kHz or MHz that you will need to convert to Hz:

1 kHz (kilohertz) = 1000 Hz	1 MHz (1 megahertz) = 1 000 000 Hz

EXAMPLE: Calculate the speed of a wave with frequency 2 MHz and wavelength 5 cm.

ANSWER: First change to the right units:
2 MHz = 2 000 000 Hz. 5 cm = 0.05 m.
Speed = frequency × wavelength = 2 000 000 × 0.05 = 100 000 m/s.

This stuff on frequency is really painful — I mean it Hertz...

Learn everything on this page, then cover it up and scribble it all down.
Then try this: A wave has a frequency of 2500 Hz and a wavelength of 0.2 m. Find its speed.*

Wave Properties

Now you know the basics, let's have a look at some wave properties.

All Waves Can be Reflected, Refracted and Diffracted

1) All electromagnetic waves (see page 62) travel in a straight line through whatever substance they're travelling in.

2) When waves meet an obstacle or new substance, they may change direction.

3) This can happen by reflection (see below) or by refraction or diffraction (see next page).

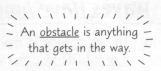
An obstacle is anything that gets in the way.

Reflection of Light Lets Us See Things

1) Reflection of light is what allows us to see objects.

2) Light bounces off the objects into our eyes.

3) A plane surface is a smooth, flat surface that reflects well, e.g. a mirror.

4) For every reflected ray, the angle of incidence (i) = angle of reflection (r).

5) You may have to draw a ray diagram like this:

The incident ray is just the ray that's hitting the surface — as shown on the diagram.

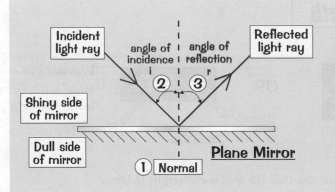

DRAWING RAY DIAGRAMS

1) Draw a dotted line at right angles to the surface, at the point where the incident ray meets the surface. This line is called the normal.

2) Measure the angle between the incident ray and the normal. This is the angle of incidence (i).

3) Angle of incidence (i) = angle of reflection (r), so draw in the reflected ray at the same angle but on the other side of the normal.

6) You might have to draw a diagram showing more than one reflection.

7) Just take your time and follow the steps above for each reflection.

8) For example, periscopes use multiple reflections in angled mirrors to bend light round corners.

9) Draw the normal and reflected ray for the first mirror, then the same again for the second mirror.

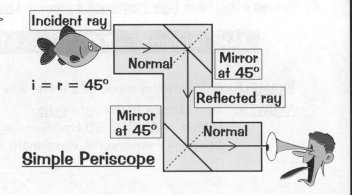

Simple Periscope

i = r = 45°

Plane mirrors — what pilots use to look behind them...

This stuff on reflection isn't too tricky — once you've learnt it of course. Make sure you take your time to draw nice, clear ray diagrams and you should be well on your way. Don't forget your ruler.

Diffraction and Refraction

If you liked <u>reflection</u>, you'll love <u>diffraction</u> and <u>refraction</u> — they're awesome.
If you didn't like reflection — tough luck. You need to know about <u>all three</u> of them. Sorry.

Diffraction — Waves Spreading Out

1) All waves <u>spread out</u> at the edges when they pass through a <u>gap</u> or <u>pass an object</u>.

2) This is called <u>diffraction</u>.
   For example, you can <u>hear</u> someone through an open door even if you can't see them.
   The sound waves <u>diffract</u> as they go through the door and fill the room.

3) You can get <u>different amounts</u> of diffraction:

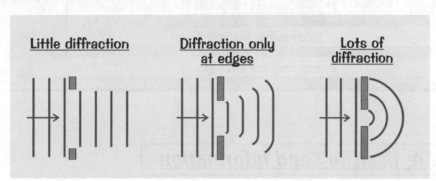

Little diffraction   Diffraction only at edges   Lots of diffraction

Changing the size of the gap affects how much it diffracts (spreads out).

Refraction — Changing the Speed of a Wave Can Change its Direction

1) Waves travel at <u>different speeds</u> in different substances.

2) So when a wave passes from one substance to another it <u>changes speed</u>.

3) This <u>change in speed</u> can make the wave <u>change direction</u> at the <u>boundary</u> between the two substances.

4) This is called <u>refraction</u>.
   For example, <u>light waves</u> can refract at the boundary as they pass from <u>air</u> into a <u>glass block</u>.

5) Waves are <u>only</u> refracted if they meet the boundary <u>at an angle</u>.

6) If they're travelling <u>at right angles</u> to the boundary they will <u>change speed</u>, but <u>NOT direction</u>.

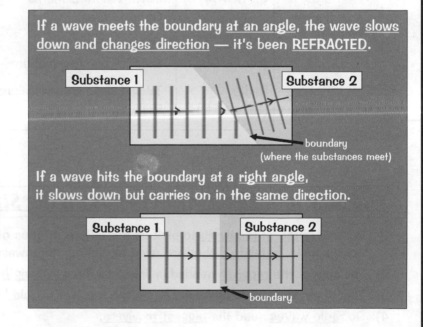

If a wave meets the boundary <u>at an angle</u>, the wave <u>slows down</u> and <u>changes direction</u> — it's been REFRACTED.

Substance 1   Substance 2

boundary
(where the substances meet)

If a wave hits the boundary at a <u>right angle</u>, it <u>slows down</u> but carries on in the <u>same direction</u>.

Substance 1   Substance 2

boundary

Lights, camera, refraction...

Remember that <u>all</u> waves can be <u>diffracted</u>. It doesn't matter what <u>type</u> of wave it is — sound, light, water.
The thing to remember about <u>refraction</u> is that the wave has to meet a boundary <u>at an angle</u> to change direction.

EM Waves and Communication

Waves are <u>brill</u>. There is <u>no end</u> to the things you can do with a wave — especially <u>electromagnetic waves</u>.

There are Seven Types of Electromagnetic (EM) Waves

1) <u>Electromagnetic (EM) radiation</u> has many <u>different wavelengths</u>.

2) EM waves can be split into <u>seven types</u> of wave depending on their <u>wavelength</u> and <u>frequency</u>.

3) You need to know their <u>names</u> and <u>list them</u> in order by frequency and wavelength:

RADIO WAVES	MICRO WAVES	INFRA RED	VISIBLE LIGHT	ULTRA VIOLET	X-RAYS	GAMMA RAYS

Increasing frequency ⟶

⟵ Increasing wavelength

Some EM Waves Are Used To Send Information

1) EM radiation has been used in communications to <u>send information</u> for years.
For example, using <u>light</u> to send signals in Morse code (see p. 63).

2) There are quite a few more <u>modern uses</u> as well:

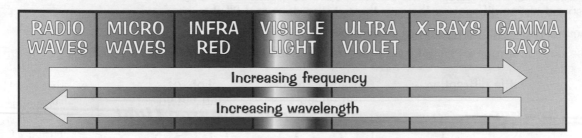

Visible light (see p. 64)	Optical fibres for telephone and broadband internet
Infrared (p. 63-64)	TV remote controls 'Night vision' cameras Optical fibres
Microwave (see p. 66)	Mobile phones Satellite communication
Radio (see p. 65)	TV and radio transmissions Radar

The Size of a Receiver Depends on the Size of the Wave

1) We use <u>different receivers</u> to pick up the different types of <u>EM waves</u> used for communication.
For example, <u>satellite dishes</u> are used to pick up microwaves.

2) The <u>size</u> of the <u>receiver</u> needed is linked to the <u>wavelength</u> of the wave.

3) The <u>longer</u> the wavelength, the <u>larger</u> the receiver should be.

4) So <u>radio waves</u> need the <u>biggest receivers</u>,
then <u>microwaves</u>, then <u>infrared</u>, then <u>light waves</u> etc.

Where would Chris Moyles be without EM waves — I ask you...

Life would be dull without EM waves — no TV, no radio, no mobile phone, no broadband internet.
You'd probably get loads more revision done though, without all that to distract you. Ah well.

Communicating with Light and Infrared

Light and infrared are useful waves for communicating — even over long distances or in awkward places.

Communicating with Light Needs a Code

1) In the past, light was used to speed up communication over long distances.
2) Messages could be sent between stations far away, by flashing a light on and off in a code.
3) Morse code was often used for this.
4) In Morse code, each letter of the alphabet (and each number 0-9) has a matching pattern of 'dots' and 'dashes'.
5) These are pulses of light (or sound) that last for a certain length of time.
6) Morse code is a type of digital signal (see p. 67) because the light pulse is only either 'on' or 'off'.

Lasers Produce Narrow Beams of Single-Coloured Light

1) A laser beam is just a special ray of light.
2) All the light waves in a laser beam are one single colour.
3) The fancy name for light that's all one colour is monochromatic.
4) Lasers have narrow (thin) beams that stay narrow, even at a long distance from the light source.
5) Because they stay narrow, the energy of the beam stays intense (strong) too.
6) These properties (narrow and strong) mean lasers can be used for lots of things:

1) In surgery	2) In dental treatments
3) As cutting tools in industry	4) In laser light shows
5) As 'sights' on weapons to light up the target.	

Infrared Has Many Uses Around the Home

1) Infrared radiation (IR) can be used to send information between mobile phones or computers — but only over short distances.
2) Remote controls send information to TVs and video and DVD players using IR.
3) Automatic doors use it too.
4) Infrared can be used in optical fibres (see next page).
5) IR sensors can detect body heat so they are used in security systems like burglar alarms and security lights.
6) When a person walks in front of the sensor, it detects their body heat and turns on an alarm or a light.
7) Thermal imaging cameras work in a similar way — they detect heat and use it to create a picture.

IR (heat radiation) is also used to cook food in grills and toasters (see p. 55).

IR Signals Can Control Electrical Equipment

1) Remote controls for electrical things work by flashing pulses of IR in different patterns.
2) The pattern of pulses acts as a code — similar to how Morse code works.
   For example, a DVD player might know that a certain pattern of pulses means play. So when it sees this pattern, it will play the DVD. A different pattern will tell it to pause, and so on.

Dynamite with a laser beam — guaranteed to blow your mind...

Compared with lasers, infrared seems a bit dull. It's still really useful though — it makes our lives a bit easier (and safer). I can remember a time before TV remote controls — you actually had to get up to change channel.

Optical Fibres

And here's more about what <u>light</u> and <u>infrared</u> can do.

Total Internal Reflection Depends on the Critical Angle

1) <u>Total internal reflection</u> (TIR) can happen when light or infrared meets a <u>boundary</u> between substances.
2) It happens when a ray goes from a <u>dense substance</u> (like <u>glass</u>) into a <u>less dense</u> substance (like <u>air</u>).
3) TIR can happen at <u>glass-air</u> boundaries, <u>water-air</u> boundaries and <u>Perspex®-air</u> boundaries.
4) It all depends on the <u>angle of incidence</u> of the ray — the angle it hits the boundary at.
5) If the angle's <u>big enough</u>, the ray doesn't come out at all but gets <u>reflected back</u> inside — this is <u>TIR</u>.
6) '<u>Big enough</u>' means <u>bigger</u> than the <u>critical angle</u> for that substance.
7) Every substance has its <u>own</u>, <u>different</u> critical angle.
8) You need to know <u>what happens</u> if the angle is <u>below</u>, <u>at</u> or <u>above</u> the critical angle:

<u>IF THE ANGLE OF INCIDENCE (i) IS...</u>

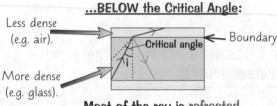

...BELOW the Critical Angle:

Less dense (e.g. air).

Critical angle — Boundary

More dense (e.g. glass).

Most of the ray is <u>refracted</u>. Some is <u>internally reflected</u>.

...AT the Critical Angle:

Critical angle

Ray goes <u>along the surface</u> (with some <u>internal reflection</u>).

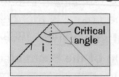

...ABOVE the Critical Angle:

I said ANGLE

Critical angle

The ray <u>doesn't come out</u>. It's <u>all</u> internally reflected, (<u>total internal reflection</u>).

Light and Infrared Can Travel Through Optical Fibres

1) <u>Optical fibres</u> can carry <u>data</u> (information) over long distances as <u>pulses</u> of <u>light</u> or <u>infrared rays</u>.
2) The ray <u>enters the fibre</u> so that it hits the boundary at an angle <u>bigger than the critical angle</u>.
3) This causes <u>total internal reflection</u> within the fibre.
4) The ray goes in at one end and <u>bounces off</u> the boundary <u>again and again</u> until it comes out at the other end.
5) Light and infrared travel <u>really fast</u> so optical fibres let you <u>send information</u> really <u>quickly</u>.
6) Optical fibres use <u>digital signals</u> (<u>on</u> and <u>off</u> pulses) so it's also <u>easier</u> to <u>remove</u> any <u>noise</u> from the signal (see page 67).
7) But as it's digital the information is sent as a <u>code</u>, so you need to <u>decode</u> it at the other end.
8) This requires more <u>technology</u> like <u>complicated receivers</u> to decode the data.

TIR IN AN OPTICAL FIBRE

less dense   more dense

boundary

ray going in to fibre

angle of incidence bigger than critical angle

If you're not sure what life's about, try total internal reflection...

Here's something to make you go 'wow' — an optical fibre which is thinner than a human hair can have over <u>one million</u> telephone calls going down it at the same time. Well I was impressed.

Wireless Communication

Shouting is a good way to <u>communicate without wires</u>. But <u>radio waves</u> are probably a better option.

Wireless Technology Has Its Advantages

1) <u>Wireless technology</u> uses <u>electromagnetic radiation</u> for <u>communication</u> <u>without wires</u>.
2) It's used for <u>radio</u>, <u>mobile phones</u>, <u>television</u> and wireless <u>internet</u> (on <u>laptop computers</u>).
3) A <u>disadvantage</u> of wireless technology is that you <u>need an aerial</u> to pick up the signals.
4) But wireless technology has <u>loads of benefits</u> too:
   • It's <u>convenient</u> (makes life easier).
   • There's no need for <u>wires</u> or a connection to a <u>telephone line</u>.
   • It's <u>portable</u> (you can use it <u>on the move</u>).

All Waves Can be Reflected and Refracted

1) Waves used for communication are always meeting <u>obstacles</u>, like tall buildings.
2) They can also meet <u>different substances</u> — like the different <u>layers</u> in the atmosphere.
3) When waves meet an obstacle or new substance, they could be:
   • <u>Reflected</u> — they bounce off the obstacle or substance (see p. 60)
   • <u>Refracted</u> — which means they <u>change direction</u> (see p. 61).
4) This can be a <u>good thing</u> for communication.
   For example, radio waves can travel <u>much further</u> because they <u>reflect off</u> a part of the <u>atmosphere</u>.
5) It can also be a <u>bad thing</u>.
   For example, <u>refraction</u> can <u>bend signals away</u> from <u>receivers</u>, so the signal is <u>lost</u>.

Radio Waves Can Interfere with Each Other

1) A <u>radio station</u> sends out <u>radio waves</u> of a certain <u>frequency</u>.
2) <u>Different stations</u> can send out waves of <u>similar frequencies</u>.
3) These waves often <u>interfere</u> (<u>mix</u>) with each other.
4) When this happens, you hear an <u>unpleasant mix</u> of two signals.
5) Radio stations <u>near</u> to each other often use <u>different frequencies</u> so they don't interfere as much.

Digital Radio Helps Reduce Interference

1) <u>Digital Audio Broadcasting</u> (DAB) has a <u>digital</u> signal rather than an <u>analogue</u> one (see page 67).
2) DAB is <u>good</u> for two reasons:
   • There's <u>less interference</u> with other radio stations than with analogue radio.
   • There are <u>more radio stations</u> available.
3) But DAB also has two <u>bad points</u>:
   • Some areas <u>can't pick up DAB</u> at the moment.
   • The <u>sound quality</u> of DAB is often <u>not as good</u> as an analogue <u>FM</u> radio broadcast.

Life's better unplugged...
Wireless technology lets you call a mate <u>**AND**</u> listen to the radio on the bus on the way home. But please don't.

Microwaves

Microwaves have two main uses — <u>communication</u> and <u>cooking</u> food.

Microwaves Carry Mobile Phone Signals

1) Mobile phone calls travel as <u>microwaves</u> from your phone to the nearest <u>transmitter (mast)</u>.
2) Microwaves <u>don't diffract</u> (bend) much — see page 61.
3) This means that transmitters need to be placed in <u>line of sight</u> of each other — this means if you drew a <u>line</u> between them there would be <u>no obstacles</u> blocking the path.
4) They're usually put on <u>hill tops</u> and fairly <u>close to one another</u>.
5) If there's a hill or something between you and the transmitter, you might get a <u>poor signal</u>, or no signal.
6) They're also affected by the <u>curvature of the Earth</u> because they can't <u>bend</u> round it that well.
7) The microwaves used for mobile phones are <u>partly absorbed</u> by water.
8) So in <u>wet weather</u>, or if you're near a <u>lake</u>, you can <u>lose signal</u> too.

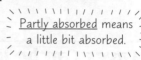
<u>Partly absorbed</u> means a little bit absorbed.

Microwave Ovens Use a Different Wavelength from Mobiles

1) Microwaves <u>penetrate</u> a <u>few centimetres</u> into food.
2) Then they're <u>absorbed</u> by <u>water</u> or <u>fat molecules</u> which <u>heats</u> them up.
3) The heat <u>energy</u> is then <u>conducted</u> or <u>convected</u> to other parts of the food to <u>cook it</u> right through (see page 54).
4) Microwaves can <u>pass through glass</u> and <u>plastics</u>.
5) So food will still cook if it's in a glass or plastic <u>container</u>.
6) BUT microwaves can be <u>reflected</u> by <u>shiny metal</u>.
7) So <u>don't</u> wrap your food in <u>foil</u> if you're microwaving it.
8) If microwaves from the oven are absorbed by your <u>body tissue</u>, the <u>cells</u> may be <u>burned</u> or <u>killed</u>.
9) Microwave ovens have to be carefully <u>sealed</u> so you aren't <u>burned</u> by the microwaves.

<u>Penetrate</u> means to pass into or through something.

Mobile Phone Microwaves May be Damaging to Health

1) The microwaves used by <u>mobile phones</u> are <u>different</u> from the ones used for <u>cooking</u>.
2) BUT some people still think microwaves from <u>mobile phones</u> and <u>masts</u> might damage your <u>health</u>.
3) <u>IF</u> they are dangerous, then people who <u>use mobile phones</u> or <u>live near masts</u> would be at <u>risk</u>.
4) You'd also be <u>more at risk</u> the <u>more</u> you <u>use your phone</u>.
5) There's <u>no conclusive proof</u> that mobile phones are dangerous though.
6) <u>Different studies</u> have found <u>conflicting</u> (<u>opposite</u>) results so scientists <u>can't agree</u> with each other.
7) The results of studies are <u>published</u> so they can be <u>checked</u> by other scientists until <u>everyone agrees</u>.

No conclusive proof means there's not enough proof to say for sure.

Microwaves — when the Queen can't really be bothered...

So <u>different types</u> of microwave are used for <u>different things</u>. Some are definitely dangerous — they'd cook you as quickly as they cook chicken — but people aren't so sure about the ones used in mobile phones.

Analogue and Digital Signals

Sound and pictures can be sent as analogue signals, but digital technology is slowly taking over.

Information is Changed into Signals

1) Information (like sounds or pictures) is changed into electrical signals before it's sent anywhere.

2) These signals can then be sent long distances down telephone wires or carried on waves.

3) The signals can either be analogue or digital.

Analogue Signals Vary

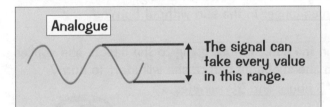
Analogue

The signal can take every value in this range.

1) An analogue signal can continuously vary.

2) This means it can be any value within a range.

3) Remember: analogue — any.

Digital Signals are Just On or Off

1) A digital signal can only be one of two values.

2) These values are usually on (1) and off (0).

For example, you can send digital signals along optical fibres as pulses of light (see p. 64), where the light is either on or off.

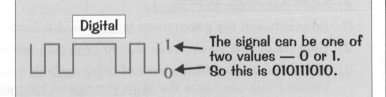
Digital

1 — The signal can be one of two values — 0 or 1.
0 — So this is 010111010.

Digital Signals Can Be Better Than Analogue

1) All signals pick up noise (interference, see p. 65) when they travel long distances.

2) It is much easier to remove noise from digital signals than from analogue signals:

This noisy digital signal... ...is obviously supposed to be this.
But this noisy analogue signal... ...could have started like this... ...or this...

3) This makes digital signals much better for things like TV and radio.

All this new technology — I really dig it all...

My gran can't stand all this digital nonsense — she still sends all her messages by carrier pigeon. Digital signals are great though, unless you live somewhere that gets bad digital reception. If you don't get perfect reception of digital signals in your area, you won't get a fuzzy signal like you do with analogue TV and radio — you'll get nothing at all. Not a jot. But then you could spend your time revising instead of watching TV.

Humans and the Environment

You've seen how <u>useful</u> waves can be — but they can also bo protty <u>bad</u> for us.

Ultraviolet Radiation Causes Skin Cancer

1) If you spend a lot of time in the <u>sun</u>, you can expect to get a <u>tan</u> and maybe <u>sunburn</u>.

2) But the <u>more time</u> you spend in the sun, the <u>more chance</u> you also have of getting: <u>skin cancer</u>, <u>cataracts</u> (an <u>eye</u> condition), and <u>premature skin aging</u>.

Premature means earlier than expected.

3) This is because the Sun's rays include <u>ultraviolet radiation</u> (UV) which damages cells.

4) <u>Darker skin</u> gives some <u>protection</u> against UV rays because it <u>absorbs</u> more UV radiation.

5) This means <u>less UV</u> reaches cells <u>deeper inside</u> the body, so it causes less damage.

6) <u>Sunscreens</u> (sun block or sun cream) also <u>protect</u> us from the Sun.

7) They all have a <u>Sun Protection Factor</u> (SPF).

8) The <u>higher</u> the factor, the <u>less damage</u> done.

9) This means the higher the factor, the <u>longer</u> you can stay in the sun without burning.
For example, an <u>SPF</u> of <u>15</u> means you can spend <u>15 times longer</u> in the sun <u>without burning</u>.

> <u>EXAMPLE:</u> Ruvani normally burns after 40 minutes in the sun. Before going to the beach, she applies sunscreen with SPF 8. For how long can she sunbathe before she will start to burn?
> <u>ANSWER:</u> Time = 40 mins × 8 = 320 minutes = <u>5 hours and 20 minutes</u>.

You must keep re-applying the suncream throughout the day to be protected though and especially after swimming.

We Know the Risks

1) Scientists and the government <u>tell us</u> about the risks of UV through the <u>news</u> and <u>advertising</u>.

2) They tell us this so we know how to <u>keep safe</u>, which helps <u>improve everyone's health</u>.

3) We're also warned of the risks of using <u>sunbeds</u> too much, because this can cause the <u>same damage</u> as <u>too much sun</u>.

There's a Hole in the Ozone Layer over Antarctica

1) The <u>ozone layer</u> is a layer of gas around the Earth that absorbs some of the <u>UV rays</u> from the <u>Sun</u>.

2) It <u>reduces</u> the amount of UV reaching Earth, so it <u>protects</u> us from <u>harm</u>.

3) Scientists have found that the <u>amount of ozone</u> over <u>Antarctica</u> is <u>dropping</u> unexpectedly.

4) The <u>low level</u> of ozone looks like a '<u>hole</u>'.

5) To make sure the results are <u>accurate</u> (spot on), scientists have done <u>many different studies</u> using <u>lots of equipment</u> to look at the ozone layer.

<u>Unexpectedly</u> means we didn't think we'd see that.

6) This helps them <u>make sure</u> that their ideas about what's happening are <u>correct</u>.

Use protection — wear a hat...

<u>Too much</u> time in the sun can help cause skin cancer, but <u>a bit</u> of sun can be a <u>good thing</u> (it helps with your body's production of <u>vitamin D</u>). So don't avoid it altogether. Just be careful when you're sunbathing.

Seismic Waves

Earthquakes produce <u>seismic waves</u> which are recorded on <u>seismographs</u>.

Earthquakes Cause Seismic Waves

1) <u>Earthquakes</u> produce <u>seismic</u> (<u>shock</u>) <u>waves</u>.

2) These can travel <u>both</u> on the <u>surface</u> and <u>inside</u> the Earth.

3) Shock waves are <u>detected</u> (picked up) by <u>seismometers</u> and recorded on <u>seismographs</u>.

4) Shock waves can cause:
   - <u>damage to buildings</u>,
   - damage to the <u>Earth's surface</u>,
   - <u>tidal waves</u> (<u>tsunamis</u>).

5) There are <u>two different types</u> of seismic waves that travel through the Earth — <u>P-waves</u> and <u>S-waves</u>.

P-Waves are Longitudinal

1) <u>P-waves</u> travel through <u>solids</u> and <u>liquids</u>.

2) They travel <u>faster</u> than <u>S-waves</u>.

3) They're <u>longitudinal</u> waves:

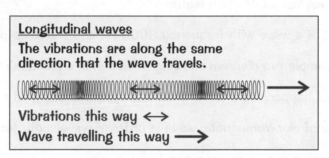

Longitudinal waves
The vibrations are along the same direction that the wave travels.

Vibrations this way ←→
Wave travelling this way ⟶

S-Waves are TranSverSe

1) <u>S-waves</u> only travel through <u>Solids</u>.

2) They're <u>Slower</u> than <u>P-waves</u>.

3) They're <u>transverse</u> waves:

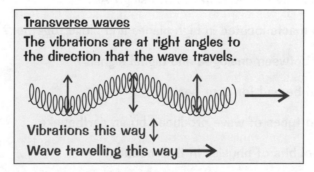

Transverse waves
The vibrations are at right angles to the direction that the wave travels.

Vibrations this way ↕
Wave travelling this way ⟶

Seismic waves — the terrible trembling truth...

You need to learn all the details about both types of seismic waves. This means knowing if they're <u>transverse</u> or <u>longitudinal</u>, if they pass through solids <u>and</u> liquids or <u>just</u> solids, and which is <u>faster</u>. You also need to remember what trouble they can cause — lots of damage and tidal waves too. So learn, scribble and enjoy.

Revision Summary for Module P1

Now a reward for getting through loads of pages of pretty tough science — a page of lovely questions. Okay, I know it seems a bit scary, but it's really important to check that you've learnt all the right stuff.

1) What does temperature measure?

2)* How much energy is needed to heat 0.05 kg of a substance by 40 °C if its SHC is 5000 J/kg°C?

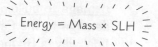
Energy = Mass × SHC × Temp change

3) What happens to the temperature of a pan of boiling water when you heat it?

4)* How much energy is needed to boil dry a pan of 0.5 kg of water at 100 °C? (Specific latent heat of water for boiling = 2 260 000 J/kg.)

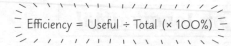
Energy = Mass × SLH

5) Briefly describe how heat is transferred through a) conduction, b) convection, and c) radiation.

6) What surfaces absorb the most heat radiation — dull black or shiny white?

7) Name one type of insulation to save energy in the home and explain how it works.

8)* What is the percentage efficiency of a hairdrier if it wastes 180 000 J of a total of 200 000 J put in?

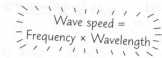
Efficiency = Useful ÷ Total (× 100%)

9) Sketch a Sankey diagram to show the energy transformations in the hairdrier mentioned above.

10) Sketch a wave and explain all its main features.

11)* Calculate the speed of a wave with frequency 3000 Hz and wavelength 4 m.

Wave speed = Frequency × Wavelength

12) Sketch and label a simple ray diagram showing reflection in a plane mirror.

13) Briefly describe what happens to a wave when it is a) diffracted, and b) refracted.

14) List the seven types of electromagnetic wave in order of wavelength (smallest to largest).

15) Is Morse code an analogue or a digital signal?

16) List three uses of infrared.

17) Describe how light can travel through optical fibres.

18) Give one benefit of wireless technology.

19) Give two advantages and two disadvantages of using DAB.

20) Why are mobile phone masts located in high places and close together?

21) What is the difference between analogue and digital signals?

22) Why can too much sun be bad for your health?

23) Name and describe two types of wave produced by an earthquake.

24) Name your top five cool bits of physics in this module.

Classification

Classification is when you <u>sort things</u> into <u>groups</u>. Biologists classify <u>living things</u> into groups all the time...

Classification Organises Living Organisms into Groups

Living things are divided into <u>groups</u> based on their characteristics, e.g. all <u>plants</u> can make their own food (see below).

1) The largest groups are called <u>kingdoms</u> (e.g. the plant kingdom).

2) The kingdoms are then <u>split up</u> into smaller and smaller groups — <u>phylum</u>, <u>class</u>, <u>order</u>, <u>family</u>, <u>genus</u>, <u>species</u>.

3) It can be <u>hard</u> to classify organisms into <u>distinct</u> (clear) <u>groups</u>. This is because <u>some organisms</u> seem to fit into <u>more than one</u> group.

4) But classification is <u>important</u> because it <u>helps us</u> to <u>understand</u>:
   - how organisms are <u>related</u> (their <u>evolutionary relationships</u>).
   - how organisms <u>interact</u> (their <u>ecological relationships</u>).

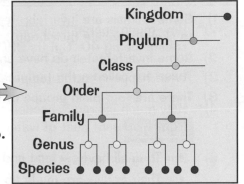

Kingdom
Phylum
Class
Order
Family
Genus
Species

Organisms are Grouped into Five Kingdoms

You need to know the <u>characteristics</u> of <u>organisms</u> in each of the <u>five kingdoms</u>:

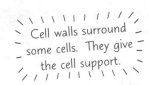
Cell walls surround some cells. They give the cell support.

1) Members of the <u>PLANT</u> kingdom:
   - Are <u>multicellular</u> (they have <u>lots of cells</u>).
   - Have <u>cell walls</u> made of <u>cellulose</u>.
   - Use <u>energy</u> from the <u>sun</u> to make their own <u>food</u> by <u>photosynthesis</u>.

2) Members of the <u>ANIMAL</u> kingdom:
   - Are <u>multicellular</u>.
   - <u>Don't</u> have <u>cell walls</u>.
   - <u>Feed</u> on other <u>organisms</u>.

3) Members of the <u>FUNGI</u> kingdom:
   - Can be <u>single-celled</u> or <u>multicellular</u>.
   - Have <u>cell walls</u> made of <u>chitin</u>.
   - <u>Reproduce</u> using <u>spores</u>.

Spores are a bit like pollen grains.

4) Members of the <u>PROTOCTISTA</u> kingdom:
   - Are <u>single-celled</u> organisms.
   - Have a structure called a <u>nucleus</u> to control the cell.

5) Members of the <u>PROKARYOTE</u> kingdom:
   - Are <u>single-celled</u> organisms.
   - <u>Don't have a nucleus</u> to control the cell.

I feel so empty inside...

The school kingdom — contains classes and student species...

<u>Classification</u> is pretty simple really — it's just about <u>putting stuff</u> that's <u>similar</u> into <u>groups</u>. Groovy.

More On Classification

After getting through that page on classification, I figured you deserved a tasty little treat. And what better than insects, spiders and crabs. To add a bit of spice, I've even thrown in some stuff on evolutionary trees...

Arthropods Are Split into Four Main Groups

1) Some animals are invertebrates — they don't have a backbone or an internal skeleton (a skeleton inside their body).

2) Some invertebrates do have an external skeleton (a skeleton outside their body). These are called arthropods.

3) There are four main groups of arthropods:

INSECTS

- They all have six legs and two antennae.
- Their bodies are made up of three parts.
- They include things like beetles.

one antenna

CRUSTACEANS

- They live mostly in water.
- Their legs branch into two at the ends — like a crab's claw.
- They include crabs and woodlice.

ARACHNIDS

- They all have eight legs (but no antennae).
- Spiders are arachnids.

MYRIAPODS

- They have lots of legs — usually between 20 and 400.
- Their bodies are made up of segments (bands).
- Centipedes and millipedes are myriapods.

Evolutionary Relationships can be Shown with Evolutionary Trees

1) You can draw evolutionary trees to show how closely related different species are to each other. It's just like drawing a family tree.

2) Evolutionary trees show common ancestors and relationships between species.

3) The more recent the common ancestor, the more closely related the two species.

4) For example, whales and dolphins have a recent common ancestor. This means they're closely related. They're both more distantly related to sharks.

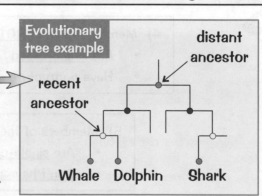

Evolutionary tree example

recent ancestor

distant ancestor

Whale   Dolphin   Shark

Every evolutionary tree has a few bad apples...

There's nothing like a few creepy crawlies to get your heart racing — and mine's pounding like a drum. That spider's just a bit too spidery for me. In fact, I'm feeling faint. Excuse me while I pass out...

Species

You need to know <u>what a species is</u> and how to <u>name</u> one — just in case you ever stumble across a brand new type of butterfly when you're exploring the Amazon jungle... or something.

Organisms of the same Species Can Breed Together

The word 'species' crops up <u>all the time</u> in biology. You need to know <u>exactly</u> what it means:

> A <u>SPECIES</u> is a group of organisms which can <u>INTERBREED</u> to produce <u>FERTILE OFFSPRING</u>.

reproduce together   children who can also breed

The Binomial System Gives Everything a Name

In the <u>binomial system</u>, each species is given a <u>two-part</u> Latin name:

1) The <u>first</u> part refers to the <u>genus</u> that the organism belongs to.
   (A genus is a group of closely related species.)

2) The <u>second</u> part refers to the <u>species</u>.

> E.g. <u>Humans</u> are known as <u>Homo sapiens</u>.
> '*Homo*' is the <u>genus</u> that they belong to and '*sapiens*' is the <u>species</u>.

3) The <u>binomial system</u> is pretty important — it's used by scientists <u>all over the world</u>.

4) It means that scientists who speak <u>different languages</u> can all call a particular species by the <u>same name</u>. This is great because it <u>stops</u> them getting species <u>confused</u>.

There's Variation in any Species

1) The <u>same species</u> can show a great amount of <u>variation</u>. For example, all <u>dogs</u> are the same species — but think how different a bull dog and a husky look.

Variation is how animals or plants of the same species look or behave slightly differently from each other.

2) But even if they look a bit different, they have <u>more features in common</u> than they do with organisms of a <u>different species</u>.

3) Similar species often share a <u>recent common ancestor</u>. This means that they evolved from the same organism and are <u>closely related</u>.

4) They often <u>look</u> very <u>alike</u> and tend to live in similar types of <u>habitat</u>, e.g. whales and dolphins.

5) This <u>isn't always</u> the case though — closely related species may look <u>very different</u> if they have evolved to live in <u>different habitats</u>, e.g. zebras and horses.

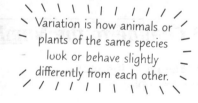

Binomial system — uh oh, sounds like maths...

There are about <u>1.9 million</u> species of <u>plants</u> and <u>animals</u> on Earth that we know of — and more are being discovered all the time. I wish I could be the person in charge of giving them all the <u>silly names</u>. For example, there's a species of fly called '*Pieza kake*' and a species of wasp called '*Aha ha*'. These biologists crack me up.

Food Chains and Food Webs

Living things eat each other. Grim, but true. And you can show this by drawing <u>food chains</u> and <u>food webs</u>.

Food Chains Show What Eats What in an Ecosystem

1) <u>Food chains</u> always start with a <u>PRODUCER</u>. Producers <u>make their own food</u> using energy from the Sun.

2) Producers are usually <u>green plants</u>, but they can be other organisms (e.g. <u>algae</u>).

3) An animal that <u>eats producers</u> is called a <u>PRIMARY CONSUMER</u>.

4) A <u>SECONDARY CONSUMER</u> is an animal that <u>eats primary consumers</u>.

5) <u>Food webs</u> are made up of lots of food chains joined together.
   Here's an example of a simple food web where <u>grass</u> is the <u>producer</u>:

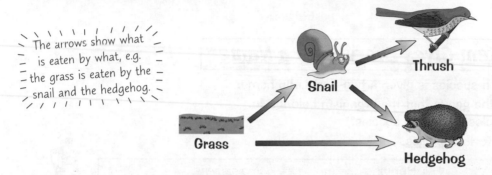

The arrows show what is eaten by what, e.g. the grass is eaten by the snail and the hedgehog.

Thrush

Snail

Grass

Hedgehog

In this food web:
- the <u>snail</u> is a <u>primary</u> consumer.
- the <u>thrush</u> is a <u>secondary consumer</u>.
- the <u>hedgehog</u> is both a <u>primary</u> and a <u>secondary</u> consumer. This gives it a <u>wide range</u> of <u>energy sources</u> and <u>nutrients</u>.

6) Each stage in a food chain or web (e.g. producers) is called a <u>TROPHIC LEVEL</u>.

A Change to the Number of Organisms Can Affect Food Chains

A <u>change</u> in the <u>number</u> of the organisms in a food chain or web will affect the <u>other organisms</u>. For example:

Dandelions

Rabbits

Foxes

If all the <u>rabbits</u> in the food chain above were to get a <u>disease</u> and <u>die</u>:
- the number of <u>dandelions</u> might <u>increase</u> as there'd be no one to eat them.
- the number of <u>foxes</u> may <u>decrease</u> as they'd have less to eat.

Sausages — my favourite kind of food chain...

Much as I love a good food chain, it's fair to say they'll <u>never win the award</u> for the <u>most thrilling topic</u> in biology. Don't forget — changes to one group of organisms in a food chain will affect all the rest. <u>Simple</u>.

Pyramids of Biomass and Numbers

Pyramids of biomass and numbers are another way of showing what's going on in a food chain.

You Need to be able to Understand and Draw Pyramids of Biomass

1) Each bar on a pyramid of biomass shows the mass of living material at that stage of the food chain.

2) It's basically how much all the organisms at each level would weigh if you put them all together.

3) Here's an example:

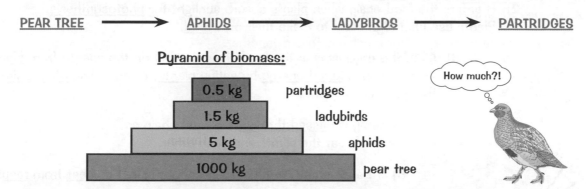

PEAR TREE ⟶ APHIDS ⟶ LADYBIRDS ⟶ PARTRIDGES

Pyramid of biomass:

0.5 kg	partridges
1.5 kg	ladybirds
5 kg	aphids
1000 kg	pear tree

How much?!

4) In the pyramid above, the 'pear tree' bar is longer than the 'aphids' bar because the pear tree weighs more than the aphids.

5) And the pear tree is at the bottom of the pyramid because it's at the bottom of the food chain.

6) To construct a pyramid of biomass you use the 'dry biomass' of the organisms.

7) This means you'd dry out all the water from the organisms before weighing them.

Pyramids of Biomass and Pyramids of Numbers can be Different Shapes

1) Each bar on a pyramid of numbers shows the number of organisms at that stage of the food chain (not their mass).

2) Pyramids of biomass are nearly always pyramid-shaped, but pyramids of numbers can be other shapes:

Pyramid of Numbers

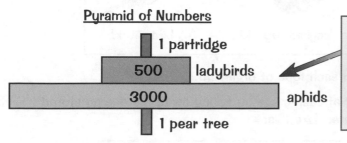

| 1 partridge |
| 500 ladybirds |
| 3000 aphids |
| 1 pear tree |

- The 'aphids' bar on this pyramid is longer than the 'pear tree' bar.
- This is because one pear tree can feed lots of aphids.
- The biomass of the pear tree is much bigger than the biomass of the aphids — which is why the biomass pyramid is the right shape.

Constructing pyramids is a breeze — just ask the Egyptians...

If you're drawing a pyramid to scale, make sure you know how much room you're going to need before you start. You don't want to draw a lovely bar for an apple tree, then realise you haven't got enough space for the earwigs.

Module B2 — Understanding Our Environment

Energy Transfer and Energy Flow

Organisms need to get their <u>energy</u> from somewhere. Producers get theirs from sunlight, but everything else has to <u>eat</u> to get it. You need to know about how it's <u>passed on</u>.

All That Energy Just Disappears Somehow...

1) Energy from the <u>Sun</u> is the source of energy for nearly <u>all</u> life on Earth.

2) It enters the food chain when <u>plants</u> absorb sunlight for <u>photosynthesis</u>. Plants use photosynthesis to make their own <u>food</u>.

3) <u>All</u> of the organisms in the food chain <u>depend</u> on the energy from <u>plants</u>. Animals can <u>only get energy</u> by <u>eating plants</u>, or by eating <u>other animals</u> that have eaten plants.

4) Energy is <u>passed through</u> the food chain as animals eat the plants and each other.

5) At each stage (trophic level) <u>energy is lost</u> as <u>heat</u> from <u>respiration</u>.

6) Energy is also lost from the food chain as <u>waste products</u>:

- <u>Egestion</u> is when food that <u>can't be digested</u> passes out as <u>faeces</u> (poo).

- <u>Excretion</u> is when the <u>waste products</u> of bodily processes are released, e.g. <u>urine</u>.

7) <u>Waste products</u> and <u>uneaten parts</u> (e.g. bones) can become <u>starting points</u> for other food chains. For example, houseflies just love to eat faeces. Yum.

HEAT LOSS

MATERIALS LOST IN
ANIMAL'S WASTE

You Need to Understand Data About Energy Flow

A kJ is a unit of energy.

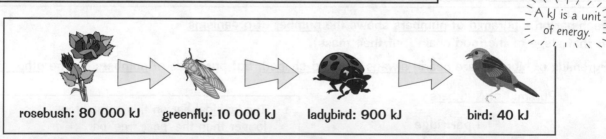

rosebush: 80 000 kJ   greenfly: 10 000 kJ   ladybird: 900 kJ   bird: 40 kJ

1) The numbers show the <u>amount of energy</u> stored in each type of organism.

2) You can work out how much energy has been <u>lost</u> at each stage by taking away the energy stored in an organism from the energy stored in what it ate. Like this:

Energy <u>lost</u> at 1st trophic level = 80 000 kJ – 10 000 kJ = <u>70 000 kJ</u>.

Energy just flows right through me...

<u>Staying alive</u> is er... dead... important, but it does use a lot of <u>energy</u>. Remember — <u>hardly any</u> of the energy an organism takes in makes it to the <u>next level</u> in the food chain (most of it's lost as <u>heat</u> or <u>waste products</u>).

Interactions Between Organisms

Organisms <u>interact</u> (affect each other) in <u>tons of different ways</u>...

Population Size is Affected By Competition for Resources

1) Animals compete for <u>food</u>, <u>water</u>, <u>shelter</u> and <u>mates</u>.

2) Plants compete for <u>soil minerals</u>, <u>water</u> and <u>light</u>.

3) Organisms compete for these resources so that they can <u>survive</u> and <u>reproduce</u>.

4) <u>Competition</u> between organisms affects:

- POPULATION SIZE — e.g. <u>lots of competition</u> might lead to <u>smaller populations</u>.

- DISTRIBUTION of organisms (i.e. where they live) — e.g. if there's a <u>strong competitor</u> in an area, it might <u>stop other organisms</u> from <u>living there</u>.

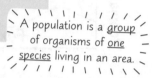

A population is a <u>group</u> of organisms of <u>one species</u> living in an area.

5) <u>Similar animals</u> that live in the <u>same habitat</u> will be in <u>close competition</u>. This is because they'll be competing for the <u>same things</u>, e.g. the same food.

Some Species Rely on Other Species for Survival

The <u>survival</u> of some organisms <u>relies</u> on the presence of <u>other species</u> — this is called <u>interdependence</u>. There are two types of <u>relationship</u> you have to know about:

1) PARASITIC RELATIONSHIPS

<u>Parasites</u> live on (or in) a <u>host</u> (another animal or plant). They <u>take</u> what they need to survive, <u>without</u> giving anything <u>back</u>. This often <u>harms</u> the host. Here are two examples:

- <u>Tapeworms</u> absorb lots of <u>nutrients</u> from the host, which can make the host <u>ill</u>.
- <u>Fleas</u> are parasites. Dogs gain nothing from having fleas — they just get bitten.

2) <u>MUTUALISTIC RELATIONSHIPS</u>

These are relationships where <u>both organisms benefit</u> — here are a couple of examples:

- '<u>Cleaner species</u>' e.g. <u>oxpeckers</u> (birds) live on the backs of <u>buffalo</u>. Oxpeckers feed by eating harmful insects that live on the buffalo.
- Lots of plants are <u>pollinated</u> by insects, allowing them to <u>reproduce</u>. In return, the insects get a sip of sweet, sugary nectar.

I compete for the best spot on the sofa...

In the exam, you might get given some <u>data</u> (e.g. a graph) showing how <u>competition</u> can affect a species' <u>population size</u> or <u>distribution</u>. If so, don't panic. Everything you'll need to know is on this page — just <u>learn it</u>.

Predators, Prey and Adaptation

A <u>predator</u> is an animal that <u>survives</u> by <u>hunting</u> and <u>eating</u> other animals.
The <u>prey</u> is the animal that's <u>hunted</u> for food and <u>eaten</u>. I know which one I'd rather be...

Populations of Prey and Predators Go in Cycles

1) The <u>size</u> a <u>population</u> can grow to <u>depends</u> on how much <u>food</u> there is for it to <u>eat</u>.

2) If a population of <u>prey increases</u>, the population of <u>predators</u> will also <u>increase</u> because there's more food.

3) But as the population of <u>predators increases</u>, the number of <u>prey</u> will <u>decrease</u> because more are being eaten.

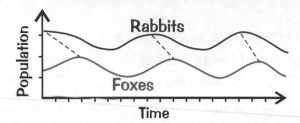

In this example, <u>more grass</u> means <u>more rabbits</u>.
* More rabbits means <u>more foxes</u>.
* But more foxes means <u>less rabbits</u>.
* Eventually less rabbits will mean <u>less foxes again</u>.
* This <u>up and down pattern</u> continues...

Adaptations Help Organisms to Survive

1) Adaptations are <u>features</u> or <u>behaviours</u> of organisms that help them to <u>compete</u> and <u>survive</u>.

2) Some animals are <u>adapted</u> to be successful <u>predators</u>. Others are adapted to avoid being caught as <u>prey</u>.

Predators Are Adapted for Hunting Prey

1) Most predators have <u>binocular vision</u> (their eyes are on the front of their head).
This means they can <u>judge</u> the <u>size</u> and <u>distance</u> of their <u>prey</u>.

2) Many predators <u>chase</u> their prey. For example, wolves often chase deer over <u>long distances</u>.

3) Some hunt in <u>teams</u>. E.g. groups of lions can <u>kill large animals</u>.

4) Others <u>ambush</u> their prey. E.g. alligators <u>hide</u> and <u>wait</u> for their prey to come close before attacking.

5) Many predators only <u>breed</u> when there's <u>lots</u> of <u>prey</u> available to feed their young.

Prey Are Adapted for Avoiding Predators

1) Prey have <u>eyes</u> on the <u>side</u> of their head, so they have a <u>wide field of view</u> to <u>see predators</u>.

2) Some have <u>cryptic colouring</u> — this means they're camouflaged so <u>predators can't see them</u>.

3) Others have <u>warning colouring</u> — this warns predators
that they <u>taste bad</u> or are <u>poisonous</u>.

4) Some species <u>mimic</u> (look like) other species which are more <u>dangerous</u>.
For example, the drone fly looks a lot like a bee, but it can't sting.

5) They often <u>live in herds or shoals</u> (groups) so there are more animals to <u>spot predators</u>.

6) They <u>breed</u> at the <u>same time</u> (<u>synchronous breeding</u>).
* This means there are usually <u>lots of adults</u> around to <u>protect</u> the <u>offspring</u>.
* And lots of offspring means there's a <u>good chance</u> at least <u>some</u> will <u>survive</u>.

Rabbits make good criminals — they're adapted to avoid being caught...

The only thing I've ever <u>hunted</u> is the <u>remote control</u> for the TV. Sadly my brother was better at it than me.

Adaptations to Hot and Cold Environments

Organisms that are <u>ADAPTED</u> to their <u>environment</u> are <u>better</u> at <u>competing</u> for resources. This means they're more likely to <u>SURVIVE</u>, <u>reproduce</u> and <u>pass on</u> their helpful adaptations to their <u>offspring</u>.

Some Organisms Are Adapted to Living in Cold Environments

Some organisms have <u>adaptations</u> that help them to <u>survive</u> in <u>chilly conditions</u>...

ANATOMICAL ADAPTATIONS to the COLD can REDUCE HEAT LOSS

<u>Anatomical adaptations</u> are features of an organism's <u>anatomy</u> (body) that help it to <u>survive</u>.
Anatomical adaptations to the <u>cold</u> include:

1) Having a <u>thick coat</u> or a <u>layer of blubber</u>. This INSULATES the body and traps heat in.

2) Having a <u>large size</u> and <u>small ears</u>. This gives the body a SMALL SURFACE AREA (compared to its weight) to <u>reduce heat loss</u>.

Some Organisms have BEHAVIOURAL ADAPTATIONS to the COLD

<u>Behavioural adaptations</u> are things animals <u>do</u> that help them survive. E.g.

1) Many species MIGRATE (move) to <u>warmer places</u> during the winter months. This means they don't have to cope with the <u>cold conditions</u>.

2) Other species HIBERNATE (sleep) during the winter months. This <u>saves energy</u> because they don't have to <u>find food</u> or <u>keep themselves as warm</u>.

Some Organisms Are Adapted to Living in Hot Environments

Many organisms have <u>adaptations</u> that help them to <u>survive</u> in the <u>heat</u>...

ANATOMICAL ADAPTATIONS to the HEAT can INCREASE HEAT LOSS

<u>Anatomical adaptations</u> that help organisms survive in the heat include:

1) Being <u>small</u>. This gives the body a LARGE SURFACE AREA compared to its weight, so it can <u>lose heat more easily</u>.

2) Having <u>large ears</u>. This INCREASES SURFACE AREA even more.

3) Only <u>storing fat</u> in <u>one part</u> of the body (e.g. the camel's hump). This stops the rest of the body from being <u>too well insulated</u>.

Some Organisms have BEHAVIOURAL ADAPTATIONS to the HEAT

These include:

1) Spending the day in the <u>shade</u> or <u>underground</u>. This <u>reduces</u> the amount of <u>heat gained</u>.

2) Being awake at <u>night</u>, when it's much <u>cooler</u>. This <u>reduces</u> the amount of <u>heat gained</u> too.

3) <u>Bathing</u> in water. This <u>increases heat loss</u>. As the <u>water evaporates</u> it <u>transfers heat</u> from the skin to the <u>surroundings</u>, cooling the animal down.

I'm well adapted for a cosy warm bed...

Remember, a <u>large surface area increases heat loss</u>. This is <u>great</u> for organisms living in <u>hot</u> environments but it's <u>not so good</u> for organisms in <u>cold</u> environments. Make sure you know which way round it goes for the exam.

Adaptations to Dry Environments

Good old British weather — if it's not raining then it's drizzling, pouring or spitting. Water is one thing we don't usually need to worry about. But lots of places on Earth are really dry. They don't have much water, so the plants and animals that live there are adapted to make sure they don't lose what little they have.

Some Organisms Are Adapted to Living in Dry Environments

Adaptations that reduce water loss help organisms to survive in dry environments.

Some Desert Plants...

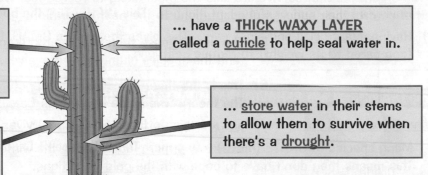

... have a rounded shape. This gives them a SMALL SURFACE AREA to reduce water loss from the surface.

... have a THICK WAXY LAYER called a cuticle to help seal water in.

... have SPINES instead of leaves. This gives them an even SMALLER SURFACE AREA.

... store water in their stems to allow them to survive when there's a drought.

... have LONG, SHALLOW ROOTS to absorb water quickly over a large area.

Some Desert Animals...

... have kidneys that can produce very concentrated urine. This means they don't lose too much water when they wee.

... have no sweat glands. This means they don't lose water through sweating.

... spend lots of time in underground burrows, where the air contains more moisture than on the surface.

That's a lovely cravat — no it's not, it's a cacti...

With all that sun and sand you'd think that desert plants and animals led a charmed life. But actually it's pretty tough. The only way organisms can survive in deserts is by having adaptations to stop them losing water. Adaptations like spines might not sound glamorous, but you need to know all about them for the exam.

The Theory of Evolution

<u>Evolution</u> is where species change slowly over time.

Natural Selection Causes Evolution

Adaptations are features that help organisms to survive — see page 78.

1) There's <u>variation</u> (differences) between organisms in a species. For example, some foxes have better eyesight than others for finding prey.

2) This variation means that some organisms are <u>better adapted</u> to <u>competing</u> for <u>limited resources</u>.

3) The <u>best adapted</u> organisms are <u>more likely</u> to <u>survive</u>. This is an idea called the '<u>survival of the fittest</u>'.

4) The organisms that survive are also the most likely to <u>reproduce</u>. When they do, they <u>pass on the genes</u> that control their <u>successful adaptations</u> to the next generation.

Charles Darwin

5) The useful genes then become <u>more common</u> in the population and the <u>species changes</u> — it <u>evolves</u>.

6) This is the theory of evolution by <u>natural selection</u>. The theory was made by <u>Charles Darwin</u>.

7) As <u>environments change</u> some animal and plant species can <u>survive</u> and some <u>evolve</u> to cope. Those that can't become <u>extinct</u> (die out completely).

Not Everyone Agreed with Darwin...

1) Darwin's theory was originally met with a <u>hostile response</u> — lots of people <u>didn't agree</u> with it.

2) This was mainly because the theory went against the <u>religious belief</u> that all organisms were created as they are now, by <u>God</u>.

Nowadays, Most People Accept Darwin's Theory

1) <u>Many theories</u> have been put forward to explain how evolution happens.

2) But the theory of <u>natural selection</u> is the one that's now <u>widely accepted</u>. Here are a couple of reasons <u>why</u>:

- The theory has been <u>discussed</u> and <u>tested</u> by a wide range of scientists, and <u>no-one</u> has managed to <u>prove</u> that the theory is <u>wrong</u>.
- The theory <u>explains</u> a wide range of <u>observations</u> of plants and animals.

For a bit more on how scientists develop theories, see the 'How Science Works' section, page 1.

"Natural selection" — sounds like vegan chocolates...

Natural selection's all about the organisms with the <u>best characteristics</u> surviving to <u>pass on their genes</u> so that the whole species ends up <u>adapted</u> to its environment. It doesn't happen overnight though.

The Carbon Cycle

Carbon and nitrogen are always moving between the atmosphere, the soil and living things. Once you've had a look at this page on the carbon cycle, flick over for some nitrogen-related fun.

Living Organisms Need Carbon

1) Plants and animals take in chemicals from their environment as they grow.

2) They use elements from these chemicals to help them make new tissues, e.g. skin and muscle.

3) Two of the most important elements they need are carbon (see below) and nitrogen (see next page).

The Carbon Cycle Shows How Carbon is Recycled

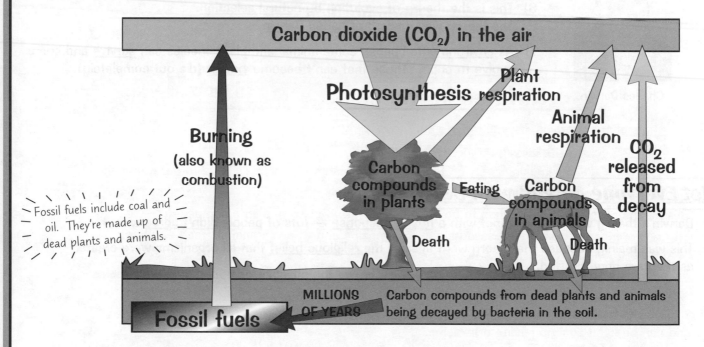

Carbon dioxide (CO_2) in the air

Photosynthesis · Plant respiration · Animal respiration · CO_2 released from decay

Burning (also known as combustion)

Carbon compounds in plants · Eating · Carbon compounds in animals

Fossil fuels include coal and oil. They're made up of dead plants and animals.

Death · Death

Fossil fuels · MILLIONS OF YEARS · Carbon compounds from dead plants and animals being decayed by bacteria in the soil.

This diagram isn't half as bad as it looks. Learn these important points:

1) Plants remove CO_2 from the air by photosynthesis.

2) The plants use the carbon from CO_2 to make plant material.

3) The carbon then gets passed along food chains and webs as animals feed on plants (or each other).

4) Both plant and animal respiration releases CO_2 back into the air.

5) Plants and animals eventually die and decay.

Respiration is the process used to get energy from food.

6) When plants and animals decay they're broken down by decomposers. Decomposers are bacteria and fungi in the soil.

7) These decomposers release CO_2 back into the air as they break down the material.

8) This process means that the carbon is recycled and can be used again by living organisms.

9) The combustion (burning) of fossil fuels also releases CO_2 into the air (see page 84).

Come on out, it's only a little carbon cycle, it can't hurt you...

Carbon is a very important element for living things — it's the basis for all the fats, proteins and carbohydrates in our bodies. The process of decay by decomposers is dead important for making sure carbon gets recycled.

The Nitrogen Cycle and Decomposition

Nitrogen, just like carbon, is always being recycled...

Nitrogen is Recycled in the Nitrogen Cycle

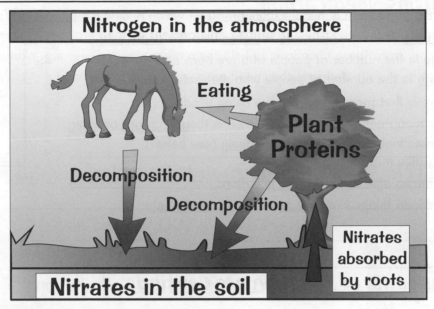

Nitrogen in the atmosphere

Eating

Plant Proteins

Decomposition

Decomposition

Nitrates absorbed by roots

Nitrates in the soil

1) The atmosphere contains 78% nitrogen gas.

2) Nitrogen gas is very unreactive, so it can't be used directly by plants or animals.

3) Nitrogen is needed for making proteins for growth, so plants and animals have to get it somehow.

4) Plants get their nitrogen from compounds in the soil called nitrates.

5) This means nitrogen in the air has to be turned into nitrates before plants can use it.

6) Nitrogen compounds are then passed along food chains and webs as animals feed on plants (and each other).

7) Decomposers (bacteria and fungi in the soil) break down the nitrogen compounds in dead plants and animals. This returns the nitrogen compounds to the soil.

8) This means that the nitrogen in the dead organisms gets recycled — and can be used again by living organisms.

Decomposition is Slower in Waterlogged and Acidic Soils

1) Recycling of nitrogen and other nutrients takes longer in waterlogged soils than in well-drained soils. This is because:

- The bacteria and fungi that decompose (break down) plant and animal material usually need oxygen to respire and produce energy.
- Waterlogged soils don't have much oxygen — so the decomposers have less energy and work more slowly.

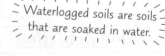
Waterlogged soils are soils that are soaked in water.

2) Nutrient recycling also takes longer in very acidic soils than in neutral soils. This is because:

- Microorganisms reproduce more slowly when the pH is too low.
- A low pH can even kill microorganisms.

Acidic soils have a low pH. Neutral soils have a pH of 7.

It's the cyyyycle of liiiiife...

People sometimes forget that when we breathe in, we're breathing in mainly nitrogen. It's a pretty boring gas, but it's vital to living things because the proteins we're made out of all contain nitrogen.

Human Impact on the Environment

Pollution is one of the hot topics in the news at the moment (literally, if you'ro talking global warming).

Human Population is Increasing

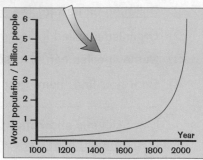

1) The world's human population is rising exponentially — which means it's increasing faster and faster.

2) Populations increase when the birth rate is higher than the death rate.
   • The birth rate is the number of people who are born each year.
   • The death rate is the number of people who die each year.

3) More people means that more resources are being used:
   • Some of our resources are finite — this means they'll run out one day.
   • Finite resources include things like fossil fuels (see below) and minerals (like metal ores).

4) Using more resources also creates more pollution:
   • Pollutants include things like sewage and household waste.

Increasing Amounts of Pollution are Causing...

1) Global Warming

1) Fossil fuels are coal, oil and natural gas.
2) When they're burnt, they release lots of carbon dioxide.
3) Carbon dioxide is a greenhouse gas.
4) Greenhouse gases trap heat in the atmosphere, which causes the temperature to rise. This is global warming.
5) Scientists think global warming could cause the sea level to rise a lot and weather systems to change. This would make it harder for farmers to produce food.

2) Acid Rain

1) When fossil fuels are burnt they also release a gas called sulfur dioxide.
2) Sulfur dioxide reacts with water in the atmosphere to form sulfuric acid.
3) This falls as acid rain.
4) Acid rain damages soils, and can kill trees and fish.

3) Ozone Depletion

1) CFCs used to be used in aerosols and fridges.
2) They break down ozone in the atmosphere.
3) This allows more harmful UV rays to reach the Earth's surface.
4) Being exposed to more UV rays will increase the risk of skin cancer.

Global warming — you might need to buy a new pair of shorts...

More people means more demand for food, energy, land and raw materials — and more waste and pollution.

Human Impact on the Environment

Human beings are <u>polluting</u> the planet — and there are a few different ways to <u>measure</u> just how badly we're doing it. Here are two of them...

Indicator Species Can Be Used to Show Pollution

1) <u>Pollution</u> can affect the <u>number</u> and <u>type</u> of <u>organisms</u> that can survive in a particular place.

2) Organisms called <u>indicator species</u> can show you if an area <u>is polluted</u> or <u>not</u>.

3) Some species can only survive in <u>unpolluted conditions</u>.

4) So if you find them, you know it's a <u>clean area</u>.

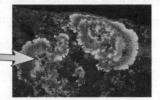

- <u>Lichens</u> show that the <u>air</u> is <u>clean</u>.
- <u>Mayfly larvae</u> show the <u>water quality's good</u>.

5) Other species live in <u>polluted conditions</u> — if you see them you know there's a problem.

- <u>Water lice</u>, <u>rat-tailed maggots</u> and <u>sludgeworms</u> all indicate <u>polluted water</u>.

Pollution Level Can Be Measured

There are a couple of ways of using <u>indicator species</u> to <u>measure pollution</u>:

1) You could do a <u>simple survey</u> to see if a species is <u>present</u> or <u>absent</u> from an area.

2) This tells you whether an area is <u>polluted or not</u>, but it <u>doesn't</u> tell you <u>how polluted</u> an area is.

3) You could also <u>count</u> the number of times an indicator species <u>is found</u> in an area.

4) This will tell you <u>how polluted</u> the area is.

There are also ways you can measure pollution <u>directly</u>, for example:

1) Instruments can measure the <u>concentrations</u> of chemical pollutants, e.g. sulfur dioxide, in samples of <u>air</u> or <u>water</u>.

2) <u>Satellite</u> data can also be used to indicate pollutant level. E.g. satellites can show where the <u>ozone layer</u> is thin or missing, which is linked to the <u>CFC</u> level (see previous page).

Sludgeworms and rat-tailed maggots — messengers of doom...

I don't envy the person that has to trudge through the polluted water looking for rat-tailed maggots. <u>Monitoring pollution</u> is important though — it can have some pretty <u>big impacts</u> — so someone's got to do it.

Endangered Species

Loads of species are endangered these days. And in many cases, it's all our fault.

Many Species are Endangered

1) ENDANGERED species are species that are in danger of becoming extinct — like pandas.
2) EXTINCT means there's none of them left at all — like the dodo.
3) Species are at risk of extinction if there aren't enough:
    • habitats — it's hard for organisms to find resources like food and shelter if there aren't enough suitable habitats to support them.
    • individuals — e.g. if there are only a few members of a species left, it'll be hard to find mates.
4) There are lots of reasons why species become endangered or extinct:

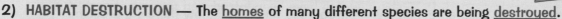

1) CLIMATE CHANGE — Burning fossil fuels is causing the climate to change. Some plants and animals can't adapt fast enough to cope with these changes.
2) HABITAT DESTRUCTION — The homes of many different species are being destroyed.
3) HUNTING — Many animals are hunted — some for food, some for fur, and some for fun.
4) POLLUTION — Pollution harms many living things.
5) COMPETITION — Competition can reduce population sizes (see page 77).

There are SIX Main Ways to Protect Endangered Species

1) EDUCATION PROGRAMMES — groups like Greenpeace teach people how to protect endangered species.
2) PROTECTED HABITATS — groups like the National Trust protect important sites such as woodlands.
3) LEGAL PROTECTION — the law can be used to protect species. E.g. it's illegal to hunt protected species.
4) CAPTIVE BREEDING — breeding in captivity (e.g. in zoos) can increase an endangered species' numbers.
5) SEED BANKS — seeds from plant species can be collected and stored. If the plants become extinct in the wild, new plants can be grown from the seeds kept in storage.
6) CREATING ARTIFICIAL ECOSYSTEMS — sometimes an artificial (man-made) ecosystem can be created. The conditions are controlled to help the endangered species survive.

Conservation Programmes Benefit Wildlife and Humans

Conservation programmes help humans as well as endangered species:
1) PROTECTING THE HUMAN FOOD SUPPLY — over-fishing means there are fewer fish in the oceans. Conservation programmes can make sure that people in the future will still have fish to eat.
2) REDUCING DAMAGE TO FOOD CHAINS — if one species becomes extinct it will affect the whole food chain (see page 74). This means conserving one species may help others to survive.
3) PROVIDING FUTURE MEDICINES — many of the medicines we use today come from plants. If plants that haven't been discovered yet become extinct we could miss out on useful medicines.
4) PROTECTING CULTURES — some species may be important to people's culture. For example, the bald eagle is being conserved in the USA because it's a national symbol.

Seed banks — watch your savings grow...

So in a nutshell, extinction sucks but there are loads of things we can do to stop it. Make sure you learn them.

Sustainable Development

It's not all doom and gloom... if we do things <u>sustainably</u> we'll be OK.

Development Has to be Sustainable

1) We need to find a way to <u>exist</u> where we don't <u>damage</u> the environment.
This is '<u>sustainable development</u>':

> <u>SUSTAINABLE DEVELOPMENT</u> means providing for the needs of
> <u>today's</u> increasing population <u>without</u> harming the environment.

2) <u>Sustainable resources</u> can be removed from the environment <u>without</u> them <u>running out</u>, e.g. <u>fish</u> and <u>wood</u>.
But we still need to make sure we don't use them up quicker than they can be replaced:

EXAMPLES OF WHAT'S BEING DONE TO MAINTAIN SUSTAINABLE RESOURCES:

Fishing quotas are limits set on the amount of fish that boats are allowed to catch.

1) <u>Fishing quotas</u> have been introduced to prevent some types of fish (such as cod) from becoming <u>extinct</u> in certain areas. This means they'll <u>still be around</u> in years to come.

2) To make the production of <u>wood</u> and <u>paper</u> sustainable, there are laws making sure that logging companies <u>plant new trees</u> to replace the ones that they've cut down.

3) <u>Education</u> is important for making sustainable development work.
If people are <u>aware</u> of the problems, they may be more likely to <u>help</u>.
For example, by,
- <u>not buying</u> certain types of fish.
- <u>only buying</u> wood products from sustainably managed forests.

Case Study: Whales — Some Species are Endangered

1) Whales have <u>commercial value</u> (they can be used to make money) when they're <u>alive</u> and <u>dead</u>.
2) When they're alive, they're a <u>tourist attraction</u> — people go to some areas just to see the whales.
3) When they're dead, people can get whale <u>meat</u> and <u>oil</u> from them, and use them to produce <u>cosmetics</u>.
4) But using whales in this way has left some species <u>close to extinction</u>.
5) Some whales are kept in <u>captivity</u> — there are <u>different views</u> about this:
- Whales <u>don't</u> have much <u>space</u> in captivity and they're sometimes used for <u>entertaining</u> people. Some people think it's <u>wrong</u> that the whales lose their <u>freedom</u> like this.
- <u>Captive breeding programmes</u> allow whales to be bred and <u>released</u> back into the wild.
- <u>Research</u> on captive whales can help us <u>understand them</u> better to help <u>conservation</u>.

I went to see whales on holiday but all I got were sheep and Aled Jones...

Whales are <u>amazing</u> animals — it'd be a huge pity if they were wiped out and weren't around for future generations. The cheeky examiners may give you <u>data</u> in the exam showing the <u>distribution</u> of <u>whales</u>. If they do, remember that the different species often live in the <u>same places</u> as the <u>fish</u> they eat — they'd starve otherwise.

Revision Summary for Module B2

Believe it or not, it's already time for another round of questions. Do as many as you can and if there are some that you're finding really fiddly, don't panic. Have a quick flick over the topics again and then give the questions another go. Good luck — not that you need it.

1) What group comes between 'family' and 'species' when classifying organisms?

2) Give two characteristics of organisms in: a) the plant kingdom b) the fungi kingdom.

3) Give two characteristics of myriapods.

4) What do evolutionary trees show?

5) What is a species?

6) In the binomial system each organism is given a two-part name. What does each part refer to?

7) What is meant by the terms: a) producer b) trophic level?

8) What does each bar on a pyramid of biomass show?

9) Below are two pyramid diagrams. One is a pyramid of biomass and one is a pyramid of numbers. Which diagram is which? Explain your answer.

a)   b)

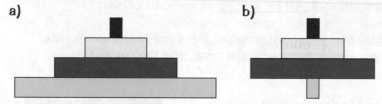

10) Give two ways that energy is lost at each stage in the food chain.

11) Explain why similar organisms in the same habitat will be in close competition.

12) What is the difference between a parasitic and a mutualistic relationship? Give an example of each.

13) What happens to the population of a predator, if the population of its prey increases?

14) Give one adaptation of: a) predators to catching prey b) prey to avoiding being caught by predators.

15) Describe an anatomical adaptation of organisms to hot environments.

16) Give one adaptation of: a) plants to dry environments b) animals to dry environments.

17) Describe the theory of evolution by natural selection.

18) Give two reasons why the theory of evolution by natural selection is now widely accepted.

19) Describe how carbon is removed from the air in the carbon cycle.

20) Describe two processes that release carbon dioxide into the atmosphere.

21) What does nitrogen gas need to be converted to before it can be used by plants?

22) How is nitrogen in dead plants and animals returned to the soil?

23) Name a gas that causes acid rain. Where does this gas come from?

24) Give one effect of pollution by CFCs.

25) Give an example of an indicator species that shows polluted water.

26) Give two ways scientists can measure pollution directly.

27) Give five ways in which we're trying to protect endangered species.

28) What is sustainable development?

29) Give one way in which we are protecting:
   a) wood resources
   b) fish resources

The Earth's Structure

This page is all about the <u>structure</u> of <u>the Earth</u> — what the planet's like inside, and how scientists study it...

The Earth has a Crust, a Mantle and a Core

1) The Earth is a <u>sphere</u> (a ball shape) made up of lots of different <u>layers</u>:

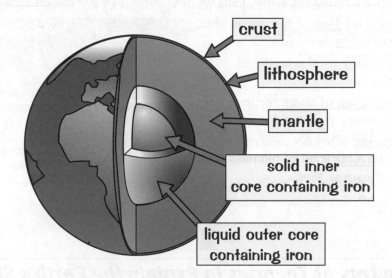

crust

lithosphere

mantle

solid inner
core containing iron

liquid outer core
containing iron

2) The <u>crust</u> is the Earth's thin outer layer. It's made of <u>rock</u>.

3) The crust and upper part of the <u>mantle</u> are called the <u>lithosphere</u>.

4) The lithosphere is made up of a <u>jigsaw</u> of '<u>tectonic plates</u>' (there's more on these on the next page).

5) It is <u>cold and rigid</u>. (Rigid just means that it doesn't change shape easily.)

6) The <u>solid</u> section between the crust and the core is the <u>mantle</u>.

7) The <u>core</u> is found in the centre of the Earth. It contains <u>iron</u>.

8) The <u>inner core</u> is <u>solid</u>, while the <u>outer core</u> is <u>liquid</u>.

Seismic Waves Can Tell Us What's Below The Crust

1) It's difficult to study the <u>inner structure</u> of the Earth — you can't get at it directly
because the crust is <u>too thick</u> to drill through.

2) Scientists use <u>seismic waves</u> (shock waves) to study the Earth's structure.

3) Seismic waves can be produced by <u>earthquakes</u> or by setting off a big <u>man-made explosion</u>
at the Earth's surface.

4) These waves travel <u>through</u> the Earth and can be <u>detected</u> by scientists
at different points on the Earth's surface.

5) By measuring <u>where</u> the waves are detected scientists can predict things about
the <u>structure</u> of the Earth.

The Crust — an awesome solid rock band...

The Earth's core is around <u>7000 °C</u> so it's a good job we've got the crust to protect us. There are a lot of new
words to learn on this page but it's all really important stuff so cover, scribble, check... Excellent.

Plate Tectonics

The Earth's surface is made up tectonic plates. These plates move around very slowly and so the world we see today is very different to what it was like millions of years ago.

The Earth's Surface is Made Up of Large Plates of Rock

1) Tectonic plates are like big rocky rafts that float on the mantle (they're less dense than the mantle).

2) This map shows where the edges of the plates are. As they move, the continents move too.

3) The plates move very slowly — at a speed of about 2.5 cm per year.

4) This means it's taken millions of years for the continents to move to where they are today.

5) Volcanoes and earthquakes often occur where the plates meet. It's the movement of the plates against each other that causes them.

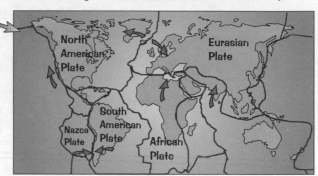

There Have Been Lots of Theories to Explain the Earth's Surface

1) For many years scientists had been trying to work out what the surface of the Earth was like and why it was like this.

2) Because tectonic plates move so slowly it wasn't obvious that they were moving or even that they existed at all.

3) So before hitting on the idea of tectonic plates there were all kinds of other theories to explain the Earth's surface.

4) But none of them were quite right...

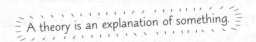

A theory is an explanation of something.

There is Loads of Evidence For Plate Tectonics

1) For a theory to be accepted by scientists there has to be enough evidence to back it up.

2) For plate tectonics there was loads of it. For example:

- Scientists found evidence that magma (molten rock) rises up through the sea floor through breaks in the Earth's crust.

- The magma hardens and forms new crust.

- This provided evidence that the continents were moving apart.

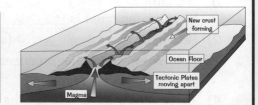

3) The theory of plate tectonics has been discussed and tested by lots of scientists. Earth scientists now accept it as being correct.

2.5 cm a year — that's as fast as your fingernails grow...

So everyone standing on the surface of our little blue-green planet is actually floating round very slowly on a sea of semi-liquid rock. Crazy as it seems — plate tectonics is the best way of explaining how the Earth came to look like it does today. Make sure you can remember what the theory is and why scientists believe in it. Great.

Volcanic Eruptions

Volcanoes occur where two tectonic plates meet.

Volcanoes are Formed by Molten Rock

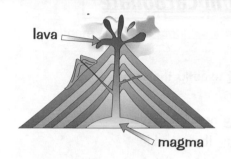

lava

magma

1) Volcanoes are formed when molten rock from the mantle breaks through weaknesses in the Earth's crust.

2) Magma is less dense than the crust so it rises up (through the crust) and spills out onto the surface where it can.

> When the molten rock is below the surface of the Earth it's called magma — but when it erupts from a volcano it's called lava.

Lava Can be Runny or Thick

1) Some volcanoes produce magma that forms runny lava, and the eruption is fairly safe.

2) Other volcanoes produce magma that forms thick lava. This causes an explosive eruption which is far more dangerous. Crikey!

3) It's important to know what type of eruption there might be so you can warn the people who live near a volcano.

4) It might seem silly that some people choose to live close to volcanoes, but there are some benefits.

5) For example, volcanic ash creates very fertile soil that's great for farming.

Igneous Rocks are Formed from Cooling Magma

1) Molten rock can cool and become solid at different speeds.

2) The rocks made from molten rock are called igneous rocks.

3) How fast the molten rock cools affects the size of the crystals that make up the igneous rock:

> Some rocks cool QUICKLY above ground. They form SMALL crystals.

> Some rocks cool SLOWLY underground. They form BIG crystals.

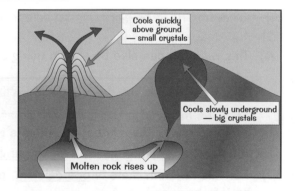

Make the Earth move for you — stand next to a volcano...

Scientists study volcanoes to try and learn enough about them to predict eruptions. It's pretty difficult at the moment — but the more they learn the easier it gets. Studying the rocks that volcanoes form also helps reveal things about the structure of the Earth. There's lots more on rocks on the next page...

Limestone and Marble

Limestone and marble are both really useful <u>building materials</u>.
And they're both made from <u>calcium carbonate</u> — how about that...

Limestone and Marble are both made from Calcium Carbonate

1) <u>Limestone</u> and <u>marble</u> are both types of rock.

2) They are <u>both</u> (mostly) made from the chemical <u>calcium carbonate</u>.

3) Even though they're made from <u>exactly</u> the same chemical they're <u>not</u> exactly the <u>same</u>.

4) For example — marble is <u>much harder</u> than limestone.

5) Limestone and marble are both used in <u>construction</u> — e.g. for making new buildings.

6) <u>Granite</u> is another material that's used in construction. It's even <u>harder</u> than marble.

Calcium Carbonate is a Compound

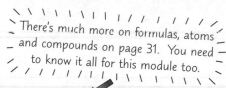
There's much more on formulas, atoms and compounds on page 31. You need to know it all for this module too.

1) Calcium carbonate has the formula <u>$CaCO_3$</u>.

2) This means it's made up of <u>1 calcium atom</u>, <u>1 carbon atom</u> and <u>3 oxygen atoms</u>.

3) Because it's made up of <u>different types</u> of atoms it's a <u>compound</u>.

Limestone can Break Down when it's Heated

1) Some chemicals break down into two (or more) new substances when you heat them — this is called <u>thermal decomposition</u>.

2) When limestone is heated it <u>thermally decomposes</u> to make <u>calcium oxide</u> and <u>carbon dioxide</u>.

3) You need to learn the <u>word equation</u> for this reaction for the exam. Here it is...

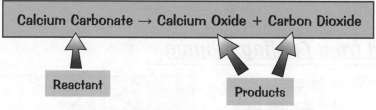

Calcium Carbonate → Calcium Oxide + Carbon Dioxide

Reactant

Products

For more stuff on writing and balancing equations have a look at page 32.

4) This reaction can also be shown using a <u>symbol equation</u>:

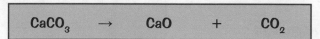

$$CaCO_3 \rightarrow CaO + CO_2$$

5) You can check the symbol equation is right by making sure it's <u>balanced</u>.

6) A balanced equation has the <u>same number of each type of atoms</u> on each side.

7) For this reaction there is <u>one calcium</u>, <u>one carbon</u> and <u>three oxygen</u> atoms on each side of the arrow, so it is balanced.

Rocks — a load of cobbles...

Calcium carbonate — what a useful compound. You need to learn the <u>word</u> and <u>symbol</u> equations on this page and remember the definition of <u>thermal decomposition</u>. Yikes. Keep reading for more exciting facts about rocks...

Construction Materials

Construction materials are the things that are used to make buildings or roads.
Loads of different construction materials are made from stuff found in the Earth's crust.

Aluminium and Iron are Extracted from Ores in Rocks

1) Ores are minerals we can get useful materials from.

2) Aluminium and iron are both metals that are found in ores.

3) They can be extracted (removed) from their ores and used as construction materials.

Glass and Bricks are Made from Materials Found in the Earth's Crust

1) Glass is made from sand which is heated to very high temperatures.

2) Bricks are made from clay which is a mineral formed from broken down rock.

3) Bricks and glass are both used as construction materials.

Limestone and Clay are Heated to Make Cement

1) Clay and limestone are heated together to make cement.

2) Cement can be mixed with sand, aggregate (gravelly stuff) and water to make concrete.

3) Concrete is a very quick and cheap way of constructing buildings.

4) Concrete can be reinforced (made stronger) by letting it set around a solid steel support (like steel rods).

5) This is called reinforced concrete. It's known as a composite material.

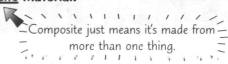
Composite just means it's made from more than one thing.

Removing Rocks Can Cause Environmental Damage

1) Rocks are removed from the ground by mining or quarrying.

2) This uses up land and destroys habitats. It costs money to make quarry sites look pretty again.

3) Transporting rock can cause noise and pollution.

4) The quarrying process itself produces dust and makes a lot of noise.

Bricks are like eggs — they both have to be laid...

If red houses are made of red bricks and blue houses are made of blue bricks, then what colour bricks are greenhouses made of? If you said green, then you're not properly awake and most likely you need to go back and read the page again. If you correctly identified that a greenhouse is made of glass rather than green bricks, then continue to the next page. Once you've learnt all the above, obviously.

Extracting Pure Copper

Here's a lovely page about <u>copper</u> and how it is <u>purified</u>.

Copper is Dug out of the Ground as a Copper Ore

1) Rocks that contain copper are known as <u>copper ores</u>.
2) The copper is often chemically joined to <u>oxygen</u> atoms in these ores.
3) Copper can be <u>extracted</u> (removed) from the ore by <u>heating</u> it with carbon. This separates it from the oxygen.
4) Reactions where oxygen is removed are called <u>reduction</u> reactions.
5) The copper can then be <u>purified</u> by <u>electrolysis</u>.

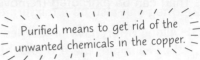
Purified means to get rid of the unwanted chemicals in the copper.

Electrolysis is Used to Get Very Pure Copper

1) <u>Electrolysis</u> means "splitting up with electricity".
2) It needs a liquid (called the <u>electrolyte</u>) which will <u>conduct electricity</u>.
3) It also needs two <u>solids</u> that will <u>conduct electricity</u> (called <u>electrodes</u>).
4) You need to be able to <u>label the equipment</u> used to purify copper.

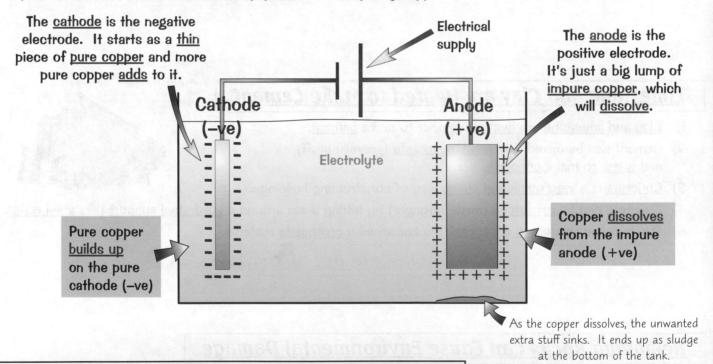

The <u>cathode</u> is the negative electrode. It starts as a <u>thin</u> piece of <u>pure copper</u> and more pure copper <u>adds</u> to it.

Electrical supply

The <u>anode</u> is the positive electrode. It's just a big lump of <u>impure copper</u>, which will <u>dissolve</u>.

Cathode (–ve)

Anode (+ve)

Electrolyte

Pure copper <u>builds up</u> on the pure cathode (–ve)

Copper <u>dissolves</u> from the impure anode (+ve)

As the copper dissolves, the unwanted extra stuff sinks. It ends up as sludge at the bottom of the tank.

Recycling Copper Saves Money and Resources

1) It's cheaper to <u>recycle copper</u> than it is to mine and extract new copper from its ore.
2) <u>Reusing</u> copper also <u>saves resources</u> as less ore has to be removed from the ground.
3) And recycling copper uses much less <u>energy</u> than is needed to mine and extract it.
4) But it can be hard to <u>convince people</u> that it's worth the <u>effort</u> to sort and recycle their metal waste. Even then you have to <u>sort out</u> the <u>copper</u> from all the other waste metal — which takes <u>time</u> and <u>energy</u>.

Revision and electrolysis — they can both go on for weeks...

Electrolysis isn't cheap — it takes a lot of electricity, which costs money. It's the only way of getting pure enough copper for electrical wires though, so it's worth it. This isn't such a bad page to learn — try writing a mini-essay about it. Don't forget to have a go at drawing the diagram <u>from memory</u> too.

Alloys

Metals are pretty <u>useful</u> on their own but sometimes mixing them together makes them <u>even better</u>.
It's just like cooking really, if you combine two great ingredients you get one seriously awesome snack.
Mmmm... Peanut butter and sardine sandwiches...

An Alloy is a Mixture of a Metal and Other Elements

1) <u>Alloys</u> can be a mixture of <u>two or more different metals</u> (e.g. <u>bronze</u> is a mixture of copper and tin).

2) They can also be a mixture of a <u>metal and a non-metal</u> (e.g. <u>steel</u> is a mixture of iron and carbon).

3) Alloys often have properties that are <u>different</u> from the metals they are made from.
For example, the alloy might be <u>stronger</u>.

4) These new properties often make the alloy <u>more useful</u> than the pure metal.

Steel is an Alloy of Iron and Carbon

1) Steel is <u>harder</u> than iron.

2) Steel can also be <u>stronger</u> than iron.

3) Iron on its own will <u>rust</u> (<u>corrode</u>) fairly quickly, but steel is much less likely to rust. (There's more about this on the next page.)

4) These properties make steel a <u>very useful</u> alloy.

5) It's used to make bridges, engine parts, cutlery, cars etc.

Brass, Bronze, Solder and Amalgam are also Alloys

1) <u>Brass</u> is an alloy of <u>copper</u> and <u>zinc</u>. It's really useful because it's <u>harder</u> than either copper or zinc.

2) Brass is used for making brass <u>musical instruments</u> (trumpets, trombones, French horns etc.). It's also used for <u>door decorations</u> such as doorknobs etc. And for making <u>coins</u>.

3) <u>Solder</u> is an alloy of <u>lead</u> and <u>tin</u>. It's pretty useful if you want to <u>solder</u> (join) things together — like electrical wires.

4) An <u>amalgam</u> is an alloy containing <u>mercury</u>. Amalgam is used in <u>dentistry</u> for filling teeth.

I eat bits of metal all day — it's my staple diet...

You need <u>metals</u> or <u>alloys</u> with <u>different properties</u> for <u>different uses</u>. For example, to make an engine part that's going to get very <u>hot</u>, you need to use something with a <u>high melting point</u>. And if you're building an <u>aircraft</u> you're going to need something that's <u>strong and light</u>. If you get a question in the exam about what alloy is best for a particular job, just use a bit of common sense and you'll be fine.

Iron and Aluminium

OK, I admit it. This isn't the most exciting page ever. But it'll all pay off in the exam if you've learnt it <u>properly</u>.

The Properties of Metals are Very Important

1) In the exam you may be asked to describe the <u>similarities</u> and <u>differences</u> between iron and aluminium — so here goes...

2) Iron is more <u>dense</u> than aluminium. This just means there's more <u>mass</u> in iron than there is in the same <u>volume</u> of aluminium.

3) Iron is <u>magnetic</u> but aluminium is not.

4) They are both <u>malleable</u> — that means they're easy to hammer into shape.

5) And finally... iron and aluminium are both good <u>electrical conductors</u>.

Corrosion is when Metals are Destroyed Slowly by a Chemical Reaction

Iron Corrodes Easily

1) Corrosion of iron is called <u>rusting</u>.

2) Rusting only happens when the iron is in contact with both <u>oxygen</u> (from the air) and <u>water</u>.

3) When this happens the iron reacts to form an <u>iron oxide</u> (rust).

4) This is an <u>oxidation</u> reaction. (Oxidation is when oxygen is <u>added</u> to or <u>reacted</u> with a substance.)

Learn the <u>word equation</u>:   iron + oxygen + water → hydrated iron(III) oxide

5) Rust is a soft crumbly solid that <u>flakes off</u> the surface.

6) This leaves more iron available to <u>rust again</u>.

7) And if the water's <u>salty</u> or <u>acidic</u> (e.g. acid rain), rusting will take place a <u>lot quicker</u>.

Rust

Aluminium Doesn't Corrode when it's Wet

1) When aluminium reacts with the <u>oxygen</u> in the air a layer of <u>aluminium oxide</u> is formed on the surface.

2) The aluminium oxide acts as a <u>protective layer</u>.

3) It sticks firmly to the aluminium below and <u>doesn't flake off</u>.

4) So it <u>stops</u> any <u>further reaction</u> taking place. This means there's no corrosion — yay.

Which superhero has the smoothest shirts? — Iron Man...

Blimey, there are a lot of facts to <u>memorise</u> on this page but just think how great it'll feel when you know them all. Try writing down all the <u>similarities</u> and <u>differences</u> of iron and aluminium, then write a mini-essay on the difference between iron and aluminium's corrosion. Isn't life grand..?

Building Cars

There are <u>loads of different materials</u> in your average car — different materials have different <u>properties</u> and so have different <u>uses</u>. Makes sense.

Car Bodies: Aluminium or Steel?

1) Aluminium has <u>two big advantages</u> over steel.
2) It has a much <u>lower density</u>, so the car body of an aluminium car will be <u>lighter</u> than the same car made of steel.
3) A car body made with aluminium <u>corrodes less</u> and so it'll have a <u>longer lifetime</u>.
4) <u>But</u> aluminium has a <u>massive disadvantage</u>. It <u>costs a lot more</u> than steel.

You Need Various Materials to Build Different Bits of a Car

1) <u>Steel</u> is strong and it can be hammered into sheets and welded together — good for the <u>bodywork</u>.
2) <u>Aluminium</u> is <u>strong</u> and <u>light</u> — it's used for <u>parts of the engine</u>, to reduce weight.
3) <u>Copper</u> is easily shaped (<u>malleable</u>) and <u>conducts electricity</u>. This makes it really useful for <u>wiring</u>.
4) <u>Glass</u> is <u>transparent</u> — cars need <u>windscreens and windows</u>.
5) <u>Plastics</u> are <u>light and hard-wearing</u>, so they're used inside cars for doors, dashboards etc. They're also great for <u>covering electrical wires</u> because they <u>don't conduct electricity</u>.
6) <u>Fibres</u> (natural and man-made) that last a long time are used to cover the <u>seats and floor</u>.

Recycling Cars is Important

1) There are big <u>advantages</u> to recycling the materials used to make cars:

> • It saves natural resources
> • It saves money
> • It reduces landfill use

2) At the moment a lot of the <u>metal</u> from a scrap car is recycled, though most of the other materials (e.g. plastics, rubber etc.) go into <u>landfill</u>.
3) But European laws now in place say that <u>85%</u> of the materials in a car <u>must be recyclable</u>.
4) The biggest <u>problem</u> with recycling the non-metal bits of a car is that they have to be <u>separated</u> before they can be recycled. Sorting out different types of plastic is a pain in the neck.

CGP jokes — 85% recycled since 1996...

When manufacturers choose materials for cars, they have to weigh up alternatives — they balance <u>safety</u>, <u>environmental impact</u>, and <u>cost</u>. In the exam, you could be asked to do the same. Sounds fun.

Acids and Bases

You'll find acids and bases <u>at home</u>, in <u>industry</u> and in <u>the lab</u> — they're an important set of chemicals.

The pH Scale and Indicators

The pH Scale Goes from 0 to 14

1) A <u>very strong acid</u> has <u>pH 0</u>. A <u>very strong alkali</u> has <u>pH 14</u>.
2) A <u>neutral</u> substance has <u>pH 7</u> (e.g. pure water).
3) The scale below is the <u>universal indicator pH scale</u>. Add a drop of indicator to a solution, then <u>compare</u> the colour it turns to the <u>colour chart</u>. This will tell you its pH.

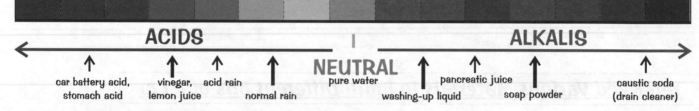

Litmus Paper can be Used to Show pH

1) The dye in some indicators will show sudden <u>colour</u> changes <u>above</u> or <u>below</u> a certain pH.
2) E.g. <u>litmus paper</u> is an indicator used to <u>estimate</u> the pH of a solution. It comes in <u>red</u> or <u>blue</u> strips.
3) To test the pH of a solution you just place the litmus paper in your solution
4) If the <u>blue</u> paper turns <u>red</u>, and the <u>red</u> paper <u>stays red</u> then the solution is <u>acidic</u>.
5) If the <u>blue</u> paper stays <u>blue</u> and the <u>red</u> paper <u>turns blue</u> then the solution is <u>alkaline</u>.
6) If the <u>red</u> paper and the <u>blue</u> paper both stay the <u>same colour</u> then the solution is <u>neutral</u>.

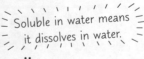

Acids and Bases Neutralise Each Other

> An <u>ACID</u> is a substance with a pH of <u>LESS THAN 7</u>. Acids form <u>H^+ ions</u> in <u>water</u>.
> The <u>pH</u> of an acid depends on the <u>concentration</u> of the <u>H^+ ions</u>.

> A <u>BASE</u> is a substance with a pH of <u>GREATER THAN 7</u>.
> An <u>ALKALI</u> is a base that is <u>soluble in water</u>.

Soluble in water means it dissolves in water.

1) The reaction between acids and bases is called <u>neutralisation</u>. Make sure you learn it:

$$\text{acid } + \text{ base } \rightarrow \text{ salt } + \text{ water}$$

2) When an <u>acid</u> is added to a <u>base</u>, we say that the base has been <u>neutralised</u>, i.e. it has a <u>pH of 7</u>.
3) If a <u>base</u> (or <u>alkali</u>) is added to an <u>acid</u> then it's the acid that is <u>neutralised</u>.

This'll give you a firm base for Chemistry...

There's no getting away from acids and bases in Chemistry, or even in real life. They are everywhere — acids are found in loads of <u>foods</u>, like vinegar and fruit, and as <u>food flavourings</u> and <u>preservatives</u>, whilst alkalis (particularly sodium hydroxide) are used to help make all sorts of things from <u>soaps</u> to <u>ceramics</u>.

Reactions of Acids

When you mix an acid and a base, exactly what you end up with depends on which acid and base you use...

Different Acids and Bases make Different Salts

1) Metal oxides and metal hydroxides are bases.
2) This means that they will neutralise acids.
3) So, all metal oxides and metal hydroxides will react with acids to form a salt and water.
4) The actual salt made depends on what acid is used and what metal is in the base.
5) In the exam you might have to name the salt produced — the clue is in the names of the acid and the base...

1) HYDROCHLORIC ACID — always produces CHLORIDE SALTS

Hydrochloric acid	+	Copper oxide	→ Copper chloride	+ water
Hydrochloric acid	+	Sodium hydroxide	→ Sodium chloride	+ water

2) SULFURIC ACID — always produces SULFATE SALTS

Sulfuric acid	+	Zinc oxide	→ Zinc sulfate	+ water
Sulfuric acid	+	Potassium hydroxide	→ Potassium sulfate	+ water

3) NITRIC ACID — always produces NITRATE SALTS

Nitric acid	+	Magnesium oxide	→ Magnesium nitrate	+ water
Nitric acid	+	Sodium hydroxide	→ Sodium nitrate	+ water

4) And finally, PHOSPHORIC ACID — always produces PHOSPHATE SALTS

Phosphoric acid	+	Iron oxide	→ Iron phosphate	+ water
Phosphoric acid	+	Sodium hydroxide	→ Sodium phosphate	+ water

Metal Carbonates will also Neutralise Acids

1) These are very like the reactions above — they just produce carbon dioxide as well.
2) So when an acid reacts with a carbonate you get a salt and water and carbon dioxide.
3) The salt produced follows the same pattern as above
   — it depends on the acid used and the metal in the base.

Hydrochloric acid	+	Sodium carbonate	→ Sodium chloride	+ water	+ carbon dioxide
Sulfuric acid	+	Calcium carbonate	→ Calcium sulfate	+ water	+ carbon dioxide

Acid + Revision → Zzzzzzzz...

Make sure you understand how all these salts are named. Try writing down different combinations of acids and bases, and acids and carbonates. Then write down the salt produced by each neutralisation. Enjoy.

Fertilisers

Fertilisers make crops grow <u>bigger</u> and <u>faster</u> — but they're <u>not always</u> good for the environment...

Fertilisers Help to Make Healthy Crops

1) There are some chemicals that plants <u>need</u> in order to grow properly. These are called <u>essential</u> elements.

2) The three main essential elements are <u>nitrogen</u> (N), <u>phosphorus</u> (P) and <u>potassium</u> (K).

3) If plants don't get enough of these elements, they <u>won't grow well</u>.

4) <u>Fertilisers</u> can be used to make sure plants get these elements.

5) The fertiliser must first <u>dissolve in water</u> before it can be taken in by the crop <u>roots</u>.

6) Using fertilisers helps to increase the number of crops grown in a certain area — this is the <u>crop yield</u>.

Fertilisers are Really Useful...

1) The <u>population</u> of the world is <u>rising rapidly</u>.

2) So we need to produce <u>more food</u> to feed everyone.

3) Fertilisers <u>increase crop yield</u>, so the more fertiliser we make, the more crops we can grow, and the <u>more people we can feed</u>.

4) <u>Ammonia</u> (NH_3) is really important for <u>world food production</u> because it's a <u>key ingredient</u> of many <u>fertilisers</u>.

5) There are loads of <u>different types</u> of ammonia fertilisers — there's more on them on the next page. Groovy.

...But They Can Cause Big Problems

1) If we use <u>too many</u> fertilisers we risk <u>polluting</u> our <u>water supplies</u>.

2) Fertilisers can also damage the <u>environment</u> by causing <u>eutrophication</u>:

- When fertilisers end up in <u>lakes</u> and <u>rivers</u> they increase <u>algae</u> growth.
- The algae <u>blocks the light</u> which the underwater plants and animals need to survive.
- As a result pretty much everything in the river <u>dies</u> (including fish and insects).
- This process is called <u>eutrophication</u> — it basically means 'too much of a good thing.'

©iStockphoto.com/Heike Kampe

The grass is always greener on the other side — my neighbour uses fertiliser...

Unfortunately, no matter how <u>good</u> something is, there's nearly always a <u>downside</u>. Make sure you understand <u>why</u> fertilisers are so important but also <u>why</u> they can cause serious problems. Learn it mini-essay style.

Preparing Fertilisers

Ammonium nitrate is an especially good fertiliser, and you can make it from a few simple chemicals in the lab.

Ammonia Can be Used to Produce Fertilisers

1) Ammonia is an alkali so can be neutralised by acids.
2) The salts that are made are called ammonium salts.
3) These ammonium salts are used as fertilisers.

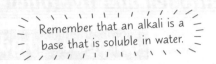
Remember that an alkali is a base that is soluble in water.

Preparing Fertilisers in the Lab

1) You can make most fertilisers using a titration — just choose the right acid and base to get the salt you want. (See below for which acids and bases to use.)
2) You have to be able to label this apparatus for making a fertiliser, but you don't need to learn the method.

funnel to pour in the acid

burette

acid

measuring cylinder to accurately measure the base

conical flask containing base

The Name of a Fertiliser Comes from the Acid and the Base Used

In the exam you might have to name the acid and the base needed to make a certain fertiliser. For example:

1) Ammonium nitrate (NH_4NO_3): (You can tell this fertiliser contains nitrogen because of the N in the formula.)

Ammonia + Nitric acid → Ammonium nitrate

2) Ammonium sulfate (($NH_4)_2SO_4$):

Ammonia + Sulfuric acid → Ammonium sulfate

3) Ammonium phosphate (($NH_4)_3PO_4$): (You can tell this fertiliser contains phosphorus because of the P in the formula.)

Ammonia + Phosphoric acid → Ammonium phosphate

4) Potassium nitrate (KNO_3): (You can tell this fertiliser contains potassium because of the K in the formula.)

Potassium hydroxide + Nitric acid → Potassium nitrate + water

Urea is made from ammonia and is also commonly used as a fertiliser.

The target has been neutralised...

There's only one way to learn this page and that's to cover, scribble, check — examiners love this stuff so make sure you know it all from memory. There's more on ammonia coming up on the next page...

The Haber Process

This is an <u>important industrial process</u>. It produces <u>ammonia</u> (NH₃), which is used to make <u>fertilisers</u>.

Nitrogen and Hydrogen are Needed to Make Ammonia

nitrogen + hydrogen ⇌ ammonia

$$N_2 + 3H_2 \rightleftharpoons 2NH_3$$

You're going to have to learn the word equation and the balanced symbol equation for the exam.

1) The two-way reaction arrow (⇌) means that the reaction is <u>reversible</u> — it occurs in both directions.

2) This means that nitrogen and hydrogen can <u>react</u> to make <u>ammonia</u> and ammonia can <u>break down</u> to give <u>nitrogen</u> and <u>hydrogen</u>.

3) The <u>nitrogen</u> is obtained from the <u>air</u>.

4) The <u>hydrogen</u> comes from <u>natural gas</u> or from cracking <u>crude oil</u> (see page 44 for how this is done).

The Haber Process is a Reversible Reaction

1) The hydrogen and nitrogen are <u>mixed together</u> at the top of the reaction vessel.

2) The <u>ammonia</u> is formed as a <u>gas</u>, but it turns to <u>liquid</u> as it cools and is <u>removed</u>.

3) The unreacted N₂ and H₂ are <u>recycled</u> and passed through again so <u>none is wasted</u>.

4) The reaction vessel contains an <u>iron catalyst</u> that makes the reaction go <u>faster</u>.

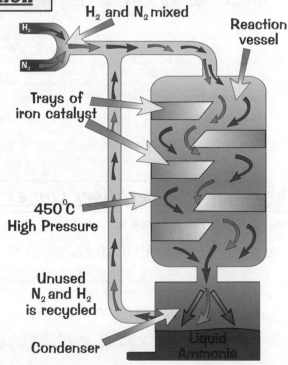

Industrial conditions	
Pressure:	High
Temperature:	450 °C
Catalyst:	Iron

Ammonia Is Really Useful

Ammonia is used to make:

1) <u>Fertilisers</u> — used to produce bigger, better <u>crops</u> to feed everyone.

2) <u>Nitric acid</u> — used to make <u>fertilisers</u> and <u>explosives</u>.

A chocolate catalyst — that's what makes me go faster...

The Haber process makes <u>ammonia</u>, which is used to make <u>fertilisers</u>, which are really useful. Learn those industrial conditions, after me — high pressure, 450 °C, iron... high pressure, 450 °C, iron... high pressure, 450...

Minimising the Cost of Production

In industry it's really important to <u>keep costs down</u> so that the business can make a <u>profit</u>.

Production Cost Depends on Several Different Factors

There are <u>five</u> main things that affect the <u>cost</u> of making a new substance. It's these five factors that companies have to consider when deciding <u>if</u>, and then <u>how</u>, to produce a chemical.

1. Price of Energy

a) Industry needs to keep its <u>energy bills</u> (for electricity and gas) as low as possible.

b) If a reaction needs a <u>high temperature or pressure</u>, the <u>energy costs</u> will be higher.

2. Cost of Starting Materials

a) This can be kept low by <u>recycling</u> any <u>materials</u> that haven't reacted.

b) A good example of this is the <u>Haber process</u> (page 102). The unreacted N_2 and H_2 can be <u>recycled</u> to reduce waste.

3. Labour Costs (Wages)

a) Everyone who works for a company has got to be <u>paid</u>.

b) <u>Labour-intensive</u> processes (ones that need lots of people), can be very expensive.

c) <u>Automation</u> (using machines to do the jobs instead) cuts <u>costs</u> by reducing the number of people involved.

4. Plant Costs (Equipment)

a) The cost of equipment depends on the <u>conditions</u> it has to cope with.

b) For example, it costs far more to make something that has to work at very <u>high pressures</u> than something that works at <u>lower pressure</u>.

5. Rate of Production

a) Usually, the <u>faster</u> a reaction goes, the faster the new material will be <u>made</u> and the <u>less</u> it costs.

b) To make a reaction faster you can use a <u>catalyst</u> (see page 39).

c) Catalysts will speed up the <u>rate of a reaction</u> which means the costs will go <u>down</u>.

d) But it will cost money to <u>buy</u> the catalyst in the first place.

This will make it as cheap as chips...

In industry these factors have to be <u>balanced</u> so you make a <u>profit</u> and provide a <u>good product</u>. You need to learn the <u>five</u> different factors affecting cost and all the points that go with them. Cover the page and scribble it all down — keep doing it until you get it right.

Salt

Salt has been used as a <u>preservative</u> and <u>flavouring</u> for thousands of years. Sailors on long journeys used to cover meat in it to keep it from rotting and the Romans even used it on their salads.

Sodium Chloride (Salt) is Mined from Underneath Cheshire

1) Salt is mainly found in the <u>sea</u> or <u>underground</u>.
2) The regions of salt found underground are called <u>salt deposits</u>.
3) There are huge deposits of salt under <u>Cheshire</u>.
4) Salt can be extracted from these deposits by normal <u>mining</u> or <u>solution mining</u>.
5) In normal mining salt is brought up to the surface as solid <u>rock salt</u> (a <u>mixture</u> of salt and other materials). The salt is then <u>separated</u> out from the other materials.
6) In solution mining hot water is pumped underground. This <u>dissolves</u> the salt and the <u>salt solution</u> is <u>forced to the surface</u>.
7) When the mining is finished, it's important to <u>fill in the holes</u> in the ground. If not, the land could <u>collapse</u> and <u>slide into the holes</u> — this is called <u>subsidence</u>.

Electrolysis of Brine Gives Hydrogen, Chlorine and Sodium Hydroxide

1) <u>Concentrated sodium chloride solution</u> is also known as <u>brine</u>.
2) <u>Brine</u> can be <u>electrolysed</u> using a set-up like this one.
3) The <u>electrodes</u> (solids that conduct electricity) are made of an <u>inert</u> material — this just means that they <u>won't react</u>.
4) There are <u>three</u> useful products:

- <u>Hydrogen gas</u> is given off at the cathode.
- <u>Chlorine gas</u> is given off at the anode. (Don't forget the lab test for chlorine gas — it <u>bleaches damp litmus paper</u>.)
- <u>Sodium hydroxide</u> (NaOH) is also formed.

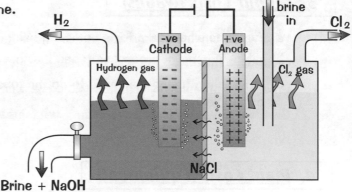

The Products of Brine Electrolysis are Really Useful

The products of the electrolysis of brine are important in the <u>chemical industry</u>.

1) <u>Hydrogen</u> is used for making <u>margarine</u>.
2) <u>Chlorine gas</u> can be used to <u>disinfect water</u>, or to make <u>plastics</u> (such as <u>PVC</u>), <u>solvents</u> or <u>hydrochloric acid</u>.
3) The <u>sodium hydroxide</u> solution can be used to make <u>soap</u>.
4) You can react the <u>sodium hydroxide solution</u> with <u>chlorine gas</u> to make <u>household bleach</u>.

Salt — it's not just for chips any more...

Salt's used for a lot of <u>chemical products</u> as well as for <u>food</u> and <u>gritting the roads</u>. There's quite a bit to learn here: the ways of extracting salt, the electrolysis stuff and all those lovely uses of the products. Oh goody, I feel a revision summary coming along...

Revision Summary for Module C2

The only way that you can tell if you've learnt this module properly is to test yourself. Try these
questions, and if there's something you don't know, it means you need to go back and learn it. Even if
it's all those equations for the reactions of acids. Don't miss any questions out — you don't get a choice
about what comes up on the exam so you need to be sure that you've learnt it all.

1)   What is the lithosphere?

2)   What type of waves do scientists use to study the Earth's structure?

3)   What are tectonic plates?

4)   Why do volcanoes and earthquakes often occur where tectonic plates meet?

5)   State the two types of lava and the types of eruptions they make.

6)   How would the crystals of an igneous rock that had cooled quickly be different to one that cooled slowly?

7)   Which of these chemicals is in both limestone and marble:
     a) sodium chloride,   b) calcium carbonate,   c) ammonium nitrate?

8)   What is thermal decomposition?

9)   What is glass made from?

10) How is cement made? What about concrete?

11) How can copper be extracted from its ore?

12) Draw and label the apparatus used to purify copper. Label the anode, the cathode and the electrolyte.

13) What two substances is steel made from?

14) What is an amalgam? What can it be used for?

15) Give two similarities and two differences between iron and aluminium.

16) What type of chemical reaction takes place when iron rusts?

17) Give two advantages of using aluminium instead of steel for car bodywork.

18) Why would copper be good for making the wiring in a car?

19) What are acids and bases? What is an alkali?

20) What two things form when a metal oxide reacts with an acid?

21) Write a word equation for the reaction between phosphoric acid and sodium hydroxide.

22) Name three essential elements in fertilisers.

23) What must a fertiliser do first before being taken up by the crop roots?

24) Draw and label a diagram of the apparatus used for making fertilisers in the lab.

25) Write the word equation for the production of the fertiliser ammonium phosphate.

26) What two chemicals are needed to make ammonia? Where can we get them from?

27) What effect does the catalyst have on the Haber process reaction?

28) Give two uses of ammonia.

29) Give five factors that affect the cost of producing a chemical.

30) Describe two ways that salt can be mined.

31) What are the three main products of brine electrolysis? Give a possible use for each of them.

Module C2 — Chemical Resources

Using the Sun's Energy

The Sun is <u>very</u> hot and <u>very</u> bright — which means it's giving out a <u>lot</u> of energy.

Photocells use Sunlight to Make Electricity

1) The Sun gives out <u>loads</u> of <u>energy</u> mostly in the form of <u>heat</u> and <u>light</u>.
2) We can use <u>photocells</u> to make <u>electricity directly</u> from sunlight.
3) Photocells generate <u>direct current</u> (DC) — the same as a <u>battery</u>.
4) Direct current just means the current flows the <u>same way</u> round the circuit all the time.
5) The <u>power output</u> or <u>current</u> of a photocell depends on its <u>surface area</u>.
6) The <u>larger</u> the surface area, the <u>greater</u> the output.

<u>ADVANTAGES OF PHOTOCELLS</u>
1) They're <u>low-maintenance</u>.   2) They <u>don't</u> need <u>fuel</u>.
3) They <u>don't</u> need <u>power cables</u>.   4) They <u>last a long time</u>.
5) They can be used in <u>remote</u> (hard to reach) places.
6) Energy from the Sun is <u>renewable</u> (it won't run out).
7) They <u>don't</u> produce any <u>polluting waste</u>.

<u>DISADVANTAGE OF PHOTOCELLS</u>
Photocells need sunlight — so they're <u>rubbish</u> at <u>night</u>, and not so good when the <u>weather's bad</u>.

Low-maintenance means that they <u>don't break down</u> easily.

Passive Solar Heating — the Sun can Heat Things Directly

1) <u>Passive solar heating</u> is when energy from the Sun is used to heat something <u>directly</u>.
2) The most obvious case is <u>windows</u>.
3) <u>Glass</u> lets in <u>heat</u> and <u>light</u> from the Sun, which is <u>absorbed</u> by things in a room, heating them up.
4) <u>Curved</u> mirrors can also be used to <u>focus</u> the Sun's light and heat.
5) A curved mirror can be used as a solar <u>oven</u>.

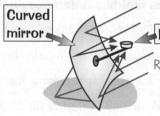

Radiation that lands on the curved mirror is focused onto the pan.

Wind Power Also Caused by the Sun

1) When the Sun heats the <u>air</u>, the <u>hot air rises</u> and cold air <u>whooshes in</u> to take its place.
2) This is a <u>convection current</u>, but we know it as <u>wind</u>. Wind can be used to <u>drive turbines</u>.
3) The turbines convert the <u>kinetic energy</u> (movement) of the wind into <u>electricity</u>.

<u>Advantages:</u>
1) It doesn't produce any <u>polluting waste</u>.
2) It will <u>never run out</u> (it's <u>renewable</u>).

<u>Disadvantages:</u>
1) Sometimes the wind isn't <u>strong enough</u> to produce power.
2) It's can be hard to find enough <u>space</u> in windy places to <u>build</u> wind turbines.
3) Some people think they <u>spoil the view</u> (<u>visual pollution</u>).

Don't let the Sun go down on me — I hate cold dinners...

It can be <u>expensive</u> to install photocells, but once you're up and running, the energy is <u>free</u> and <u>running costs</u> are <u>very low</u>. It's even <u>better</u> if you live somewhere that's <u>sunny</u> most of the time. Not Britain then.

Producing and Distributing Electricity

Most electricity is generated in <u>power stations</u> and then <u>distributed</u> (sent out) via the <u>National Grid</u>.

The National Grid Connects Power Stations to Consumers

AC is on the next page.

1) The <u>National Grid</u> is the network of <u>power lines</u> which covers <u>the whole country</u>.
2) It takes electricity with <u>alternating</u> current (AC) from <u>power stations</u> to consumers.
3) Consumers are the people that use the electricity in <u>homes</u>, <u>factories</u>, <u>offices</u> and <u>farms</u>.
4) Power can be <u>generated</u> anywhere on the grid, and then <u>sent</u> anywhere else on the grid.

All Power Stations are Pretty Much the Same

<u>Power stations</u> <u>convert</u> (change) one kind of energy into <u>electricity</u>. Usually this is done in <u>three stages</u>:

1) Energy from the <u>fuel</u> (which is usually <u>burnt</u> in a boiler) makes <u>steam</u> from water.
2) The <u>steam</u> turns a <u>turbine</u>.
3) A <u>generator</u> makes <u>electricity</u> from the movement (<u>kinetic</u> energy) of the turbine (see next page).

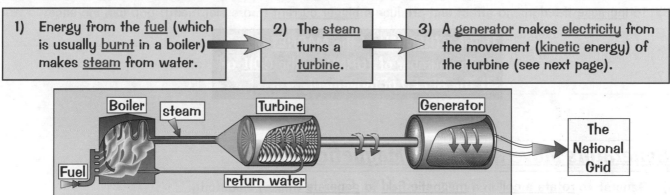

Most fuels <u>release energy</u> as <u>heat</u>. It's just the <u>type</u> of fuel used that changes. The three common types are:
1. <u>Fossil</u> fuels — <u>coal</u>, <u>oil</u>, <u>natural gas</u>,
2. <u>Nuclear</u> fuels — <u>uranium</u> and <u>plutonium</u>,
3. <u>Biomass</u> — <u>wood</u>, <u>straw</u>, <u>manure</u>.

Different Power Sources Have Advantages and Disadvantages

You need to learn the <u>advantages</u> and <u>disadvantages</u> of different fuels and power sources:

FOSSIL FUELS
1) Fossil fuels are <u>burnt</u> to release energy as heat.
2) They produce a lot of energy and power stations that use them are <u>easy</u> to set up.
3) But burning fossil fuels produces <u>carbon dioxide</u> (see p. 111) and other <u>pollution</u>.
4) We buy most of our fossil fuels from other countries so we don't control the <u>price</u> or <u>supply</u>.
5) And they're <u>non-renewable</u> — they'll <u>run out</u> eventually.

NUCLEAR Nuclear fuel releases energy as <u>heat</u>. The advantages and disadvantages are on p. 113.

BIOMASS
1) Biomass is stuff from <u>plants</u> (like straw) or <u>animals</u> (their <u>poo</u>) that can be <u>burnt</u>.
2) Biomass is <u>renewable</u> — it won't run out.
3) Biomass is '<u>carbon neutral</u>' — burning them produces <u>carbon dioxide</u>, but the amount is the same as the plants took <u>out</u> of the atmosphere when they were growing. So the <u>amount</u> of carbon dioxide taken in and released is <u>balanced overall</u>.
4) We don't need to <u>buy</u> straw and poo from other countries, so we <u>control</u> the price.
5) But you need a <u>lot</u> of biomass to produce the same amount of energy as <u>fossil fuels</u>.
6) You need <u>lots of room</u> to produce biomass, so <u>forests</u> may be <u>cleared</u> to make the room. Boo.

SOLAR AND WIND POWER <u>Solar power</u> from <u>photocells</u> and <u>wind power</u> are covered on page 106.

Power stations — nothing to get steamed up about...
Make sure you can list the advantages and disadvantages of all the different power sources listed on this page.

The Dynamo Effect

Electricity can be generated by moving a coil of wire near a magnet. Handy.

The Dynamo Effect — Move the Wire or the Magnet

1) The dynamo effect transforms kinetic energy into electrical energy.

2) Electricity can be produced by moving a coil of wire near a magnet.

3) Or it can be made by moving a magnet near a coil of wire.

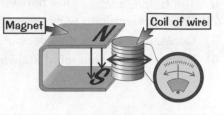

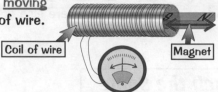

4) If the direction of movement is reversed then the voltage and current of the electricity will be reversed too.

5) To increase the dynamo effect and produce a bigger current (more electricity) you can increase:

> 1) The **STRENGTH** of the **MAGNET** or,
> 2) The number of **TURNS** on the **COIL** or,
> 3) The **SPEED** of movement.

Generators Move a Coil in a Magnetic Field

1) Generators rotate a coil in a magnetic field to generate (make) electricity.

Magnets have an invisible area around them called a magnetic field that affects things like wires.

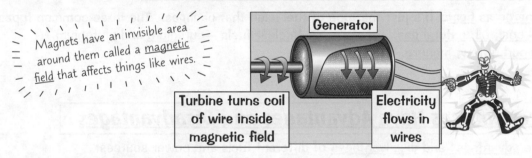

Turbine turns coil of wire inside magnetic field

Electricity flows in wires

2) Every half-turn of the coil the electric current swaps direction.

3) Think about one bit of the coil — sometimes it's heading towards the North pole, sometimes it's heading for the South pole.

4) It changes every half-turn — this is what makes the electric current swap direction.

5) So the generators produce an alternating (AC) current.

6) This is completely different from the DC electricity supplied by batteries and photocells.

7) If you looked at AC current (or voltage) on a display, you'd see something like this.

8) Turning the coil faster produces more peaks and a higher voltage too.

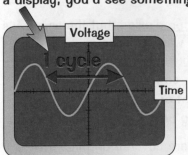

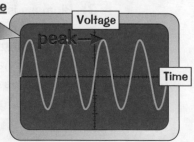

A conductor moving in a field — must be an open-air concert...

The dynamo effect is a weird thing, but important — this is how all our mains electricity is generated.

Supplying Electricity Efficiently

Sending electricity round the country is best done at a <u>high voltage</u>.

Electricity is Sent Around the Country at a High Voltage

1) You can <u>distribute</u> (send out) electricity out at either a <u>high voltage</u> or a <u>high current</u>.

2) At a <u>high current</u>, the cable carrying the electricity would get very <u>hot</u>.

3) This would <u>waste</u> a lot of energy as <u>heat</u> and so waste <u>money</u>.

4) So it's <u>cheaper</u> and <u>wastes less energy</u> to send electricity around the country at a high <u>voltage</u>.

5) This is because a high voltage makes the <u>current low</u>.

6) A <u>transformer</u> is used to increase the voltage.

7) Transformers are also used to <u>decrease</u> the voltage to a safe level before it's <u>used</u> in homes and offices.

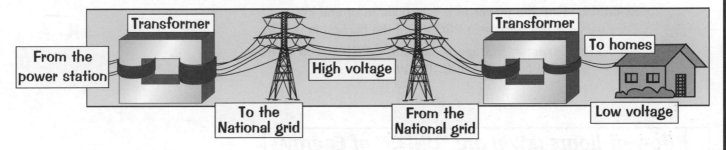

Power Stations aren't Very Efficient

1) Generating and supplying electricity <u>isn't</u> very efficient.

2) Most of the energy produced in power stations is <u>wasted</u> as <u>heat and noise</u>.

3) The total energy produced is broken down into <u>two parts</u> — the <u>useful bit</u> and the <u>wasted bit</u>.

4) <u>Useful energy = total energy – wasted energy</u>.

5) There's an equation for working out <u>efficiency</u>:

$$\text{Efficiency} = \frac{\text{USEFUL Energy OUTPUT}}{\text{TOTAL Energy INPUT}} \ (\times \ 100\%)$$

6) <u>100%</u> efficiency means <u>no energy is wasted</u>.

7) You can also show efficiency as a <u>ratio</u> by <u>ignoring</u> the '<u>× 100%</u>' bit of the equation.

EXAMPLE: A power station uses 650 MJ (650 000 000 J) of energy to generate 200 MJ of electrical energy per second. Calculate the efficiency of the power station.

The units could be MJ, J, W, MW — just make sure they're the same for both numbers before dividing.

ANSWER: Efficiency = useful energy output ÷ total energy input = 200 ÷ 650 = <u>0.3077</u>
Convert efficiency to a percentage by multiplying by 100, so 0.3077 = <u>30.77%</u>

All that energy — straight down the grid...

Once you've <u>generated</u> all that electricity, you don't want to <u>waste it</u> by heating up miles and miles of power cables when you're <u>distributing</u> it. So keep the <u>current</u> in the power cables <u>low</u>, and make the voltage <u>high</u>.

Power

Electrical power is the <u>amount of energy used per second</u>. It's a hoot.

Running Costs Depend on an Appliance's Power

1) Power is measured in <u>watts</u> (W) or <u>kilowatts</u> (kW).

2) <u>1 kW</u> = <u>1000 W</u>.

3) An appliance with a <u>high</u> power uses <u>more</u> energy <u>per second</u> than something with a lower power.

> Things that need electrical energy to work are usually called <u>components</u>, <u>devices</u> or <u>appliances</u>.

4) So <u>high-power</u> appliances <u>cost more</u> to use because they use <u>more energy</u>.

5) The <u>power</u> of an appliance can be found using this equation:

$$\textbf{Power (in W) = Voltage (in V)} \times \textbf{Current (in A)}$$

EXAMPLE: Find the power of a light bulb, in W and kW, if the voltage is 230 V and the current is 0.5 A.

ANSWER: Power = Voltage × Current = 230 × 0.5 = 115 W
115 W ÷ 1000 = 0.115 kW

Kilowatt-hours (kWh) are "UNITS" of Energy

1) Your electricity meter records how much <u>energy</u> you use in units of <u>kilowatt-hours</u>, or <u>kWh</u>.

2) A <u>kilowatt-hour</u> is the amount of electrical energy used by a <u>1 kW appliance</u> left on for <u>1 hour</u>.

3) The <u>cost</u> of using an appliance depends on its <u>operating power</u> and <u>how long it's on for</u>.

4) The <u>higher</u> its operating power and the <u>longer</u> it's on, the <u>more</u> it costs.

5) You can calculate the <u>amount of energy</u> an appliance uses in kWh using this equation:

$$\textbf{UNITS OF ENERGY} \ = \ \textbf{POWER} \ \times \ \textbf{TIME}$$
$$\text{(in kWh)} \qquad \text{(in kW)} \qquad \text{(in hours)}$$

6) You can calculate the <u>cost</u> of using an appliance with this equation:

$$\textbf{COST} \ = \ \textbf{NUMBER OF kWh} \ \times \ \textbf{PRICE PER kWh}$$

7) With questions on the cost of electricity, you'll probably have to work out <u>how many</u> kilowatt-hours have been used, then <u>multiply</u> this number by the <u>price per unit</u> (the price per <u>kWh</u>).

EXAMPLE: Find the cost of leaving a 60 W light bulb on for 30 minutes if 1 kWh costs 10p.

ANSWER: First change 60 W into kW:
60 W = 60 ÷ 1000 kW = 0.06 kW
Then change minutes into hours:
30 mins ÷ 60 mins = 0.5 h
Energy = Power × Time = 0.06 kW × 0.5 h = 0.03 kWh
Cost = number of kWh × price per kWh = 0.03 × 10p = 0.3p

Watt's the answer — well, part of it...

Get a bit of <u>practice</u> with the equations in those lovely bright red boxes, and try these questions:
1) A kettle uses a current of 12 A from the 230 V mains supply. Calculate its power in kilowatts.*
2) How many kWh of energy would the kettle use if you ran it for 3 minutes?*

*Answers on page 124.

The Greenhouse Effect

The atmosphere <u>keeps us warm</u> by <u>trapping heat</u>.

Infrared Radiation is Absorbed by the Atmosphere

1) The Earth is surrounded by an <u>atmosphere</u> made up of different <u>gases</u> — the <u>air</u>.
2) Most <u>wavelengths</u> of electromagnetic radiation <u>pass through</u> the atmosphere <u>easily</u>.
3) But the gases in the atmosphere <u>absorb</u> some wavelengths like <u>infrared</u>.

The Greenhouse Effect Helps Regulate Earth's Temperature

1) The Earth <u>absorbs radiation</u> from the <u>Sun</u>, which warms the Earth's surface up.
2) The Earth then <u>gives off</u> some of this heat, which tends to <u>cool</u> it down.
3) Some of the heat given off by the Earth is <u>absorbed</u> by <u>greenhouse gases</u> in the Earth's atmosphere.
4) These gases <u>stop</u> the heat from radiating back into <u>space</u>.
5) So the atmosphere acts as an <u>insulating</u> layer, stopping the Earth losing all its heat at night.
6) This is known as the <u>greenhouse effect</u>.

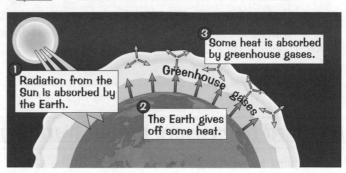

① Radiation from the Sun is absorbed by the Earth.
② The Earth gives off some heat.
③ Some heat is absorbed by greenhouse gases.
Greenhouse gases

There are Natural and Man-Made Sources of Greenhouse Gases

1) <u>Carbon dioxide</u>, <u>methane</u> and <u>water vapour</u> are all greenhouse gases.
2) They come from <u>natural</u> and <u>man-made</u> sources.

CARBON DIOXIDE

Man-made sources
1) <u>Burning fossil fuels</u>.
2) <u>Chopping down</u> and burning trees.

Natural sources
1) <u>Respiration</u> in animals and plants.
2) <u>Volcanic eruptions</u>.

<u>Respiration</u> is the process in plants and animals that <u>releases energy</u> and gives out <u>carbon dioxide as waste</u>.

METHANE

Man-made sources
1) <u>Cattle</u> farming — cattle <u>digestion</u> produces <u>methane</u>.
2) Waste in <u>landfill</u> sites produces methane.

Natural sources
1) <u>Volcanoes</u>
2) <u>Wetlands</u>
3) Digestion in wild <u>animals</u>.

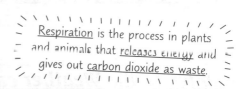

WATER VAPOUR

Man-made sources
1) <u>Power stations</u>.

Natural sources
1) <u>Oceans</u>, seas, rivers and lakes.

A biologist, a chemist and a physicist walk into a greenhouse...

...it works out badly. You need to know <u>what</u> greenhouse gases are and <u>where</u> they come from. Learn it well.

Global Warming and Climate Change

Without any greenhouse gases in the atmosphere, the Earth would be colder than it is now.
So we <u>need</u> the greenhouse effect — just <u>not too much</u> of it.

Upsetting the Greenhouse Effect Has Led to Global Warming

1) Over the last 200 years or so, the amount of <u>carbon dioxide</u> (CO_2) in the atmosphere has been <u>rising</u>.

2) The <u>global temperature</u> has also risen during this time — this is <u>global warming</u>.

3) There's lots of <u>evidence</u> that the <u>rise</u> in carbon dioxide has increased the <u>greenhouse effect</u>, causing <u>global warming</u>.

4) <u>More</u> carbon dioxide means <u>less heat</u> escapes the atmosphere, so the <u>temperature</u> of the Earth <u>increases</u>.

5) So there's now a scientific <u>agreement</u> that <u>humans</u> are causing global warming.

6) Global warming is a type of <u>climate change</u> and it also causes other types. For example, changes in the <u>weather</u> (see below).

7) Carbon dioxide levels are rising for <u>three reasons</u>:

- <u>Increased carbon dioxide emissions</u> — burning <u>fossil fuels</u> releases carbon dioxide.
- <u>Increased energy usage</u> — we use more <u>electrical gadgets</u>, and travel more in <u>cars</u> and <u>planes</u>. To produce the extra energy we burn fossil fuels, which releases carbon dioxide.
- <u>Deforestation</u> — carbon dioxide is <u>released</u> when trees are <u>chopped down</u> and <u>burnt</u> to clear land.

It's Hard to Measure Global Warming

1) It's <u>hard</u> to <u>measure</u> the temperature of the globe:

- A temperature increase in <u>one place</u> doesn't mean the temperature has risen <u>globally</u> (everywhere).
- We have fairly <u>accurate</u> (spot on) <u>temperature records</u> for the last 100 years. But they're <u>not</u> as accurate before then, because we have to <u>calculate</u> the temperature <u>indirectly</u> from things like <u>ice cores</u>.

2) But scientists are pretty sure the global temperature <u>has increased</u> because they've <u>shared</u> their data and the results are all fairly <u>similar</u>.

3) Sharing data (see p. 1) means scientists can check their <u>data and conclusions</u> are <u>accurate</u> and <u>reproducible</u>.

> <u>Indirectly</u> means working it out from other data. <u>Directly</u> would mean measuring something e.g. using a thermometer.

Changes to the Weather can have Human and Natural Causes

1) The climate is very <u>complicated</u>.

2) Changes in the <u>atmosphere</u>, <u>oceans</u> and <u>land</u> all affect each other.

3) Changes in temperature can have <u>large effects</u> on the weather. For example, many regions will suffer longer, hotter <u>droughts</u> because of global warming.

> A <u>drought</u> is when it doesn't rain for a long time.

4) Temperature change, and so <u>changes to the weather</u>, can have both <u>human</u> and <u>natural causes</u>:

HUMAN CAUSE	NATURAL CAUSE
<u>Soot</u> and gases produced by <u>factories</u> can reflect heat from cities back down to Earth. This can cause <u>increases</u> in local temperature.	<u>Ash</u> and gases thrown into the atmosphere by <u>volcanoes</u> can reflect radiation from the Sun back into space. This can cause the Earth to <u>cool down</u>.

It's getting a bit too hot in here...

People can be very opinionated about global warming — they have strong feelings about it. Make sure you can tell the difference between <u>opinion</u> (what someone thinks) and <u>evidence-based facts</u> (facts supported by data).

Nuclear Radiation and Power

Sometimes the <u>nucleus</u> (middle) of an atom spits out <u>particles</u> or <u>energy</u>.
The stuff that gets spat out is called <u>nuclear radiation</u>. It can be <u>useful</u> and <u>dangerous</u>.

There are Three Kinds of Nuclear Radiation

1) <u>Radioactive materials</u> give out nuclear radiation over time.

2) The <u>three</u> kinds of nuclear radiation are <u>alpha</u>, <u>beta</u> and <u>gamma</u>.

3) All three kinds of radiation can cause <u>ionisation</u>.

4) This is when the radiation causes atoms to <u>lose</u> or <u>gain</u> <u>electrons</u>, turning those atoms into <u>ions</u>.

5) <u>Positive</u> ions are formed when atoms <u>lose</u> electrons.

6) <u>Negative</u> ions are formed when atoms <u>gain</u> electrons.

7) <u>Ionisation</u> is <u>harmful</u> because it can <u>damage living cells</u> and cause <u>cancer</u>.

8) But nuclear radiation can also be <u>useful</u> (see next page).

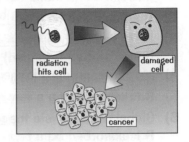

Nuclear Power Uses Uranium as Fuel

1) A <u>nuclear power station</u> uses <u>uranium fuel</u> to produce <u>heat</u> to drive turbines and make <u>electricity</u>.

2) Nuclear power has some <u>ADVANTAGES</u>.

3) Nuclear power <u>doesn't</u> produce any <u>greenhouse gases</u>, which cause <u>global warming</u>.

4) Nuclear fuel is <u>fairly cheap</u> and there's still quite <u>a lot left</u>.

3) But nuclear power also has some <u>DISADVANTAGES</u>.

4) Uranium is <u>non-renewable</u>, so it will <u>run out</u> one day.

5) Nuclear power produces <u>radioactive waste</u> that's <u>dangerous</u> because it is <u>harmful</u>.

6) Radioactive waste also stays radioactive for a long time so it's difficult to <u>get rid of</u>.

7) <u>Low-level</u> radioactive waste can be <u>buried</u> in secure <u>landfill</u> sites.

8) <u>High-level</u> radioactive waste is often sealed into <u>glass blocks</u>, which are then buried <u>deep</u> underground.

9) There is a <u>risk</u> radioactive waste could <u>leak out</u> during an accident at a power station or in storage.

10) Some radioactive waste can be <u>reprocessed</u> (recycled) into useful radioactive material.

11) <u>Plutonium</u>, that can be used to make <u>nuclear weapons</u>, is also a waste product of nuclear power.

> <u>High-level</u> and <u>low-level</u> tell you <u>how radioactive</u> the waste is.

You Should Always Protect Yourself from Nuclear Radiation

1) Radioactive materials you use need to be <u>stored</u> safely in a <u>labelled</u> and <u>shielded</u> box. (A shielded box <u>doesn't</u> let radiation <u>out</u> of it.)

2) Keep your <u>exposure time</u> as <u>short</u> as possible.

3) Handle radioactive materials with <u>tongs</u>.

4) Keep them at <u>arm's length</u>, so they're as <u>far</u> from the body as possible.

5) Wear <u>protective clothing</u> to prevent contact with your body.

> <u>Exposure time</u> is how <u>long</u> you're around the radioactive material.

Radioactive sources — don't put them on your chips...

Some people say we shouldn't build any more nuclear power stations — if we can't deal safely with the radioactive waste we've got <u>now</u>, we certainly shouldn't make lots <u>more</u>. Other people say that nuclear power is the only way to produce enough energy for all of us without causing more <u>global warming</u>.

Uses of Nuclear Radiation

Nuclear radiation can be very <u>dangerous</u>. But it can be very <u>useful</u> too.

Different Types of Radiation have Different Penetrating Powers

1) Different types of radiation can pass <u>further</u> through some materials than others.
2) They can also be <u>absorbed</u> by <u>different</u> materials.
3) <u>Alpha</u> radiation is the <u>least</u> penetrating. It is <u>absorbed</u> (stopped) by a <u>few sheets of paper</u>.
4) <u>Beta</u> radiation is a little bit more penetrating. It is absorbed by a <u>few mm of aluminium</u>.
5) <u>Gamma</u> radiation is the <u>most</u> penetrating. It is absorbed by a <u>few centimetres of lead</u>.

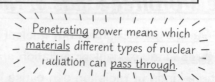
<u>Penetrating</u> power means which <u>materials</u> different types of nuclear radiation can <u>pass through</u>.

Sheets of paper stop ALPHA | Thin aluminium stops BETA | Lead stops GAMMA

Alpha Radiation is Used in Smoke Detectors

1) Smoke detectors have a weak source of <u>alpha-radiation</u> inside them.
2) If there's a fire the <u>smoke</u> <u>absorbs</u> the <u>alpha-radiation</u> and the <u>alarm sounds</u>.

Beta Radiation is Used in Tracers and Thickness Gauges

Gauges <u>measure</u> things like <u>thickness</u>.

1) Substances that give out beta radiation can be used in <u>hospitals</u> as <u>tracers</u>.
2) Tracers show if the body's <u>working properly</u> or not.
3) They are <u>eaten</u> or <u>injected</u> into the body and <u>detected</u> on the <u>outside</u> of the body using a detector.
4) <u>Beta radiation</u> is also used in paper <u>thickness control</u>:
   - You direct beta radiation <u>through</u> paper and put a <u>detector</u> on the <u>other side</u>.
   - If the amount of radiation <u>detected</u> goes <u>down</u>, it means the paper's coming out <u>too thick</u>.
   - If the reading goes <u>up</u>, the paper's <u>too thin</u>.

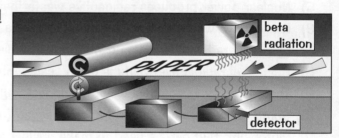

Gamma Radiation Has Medical and Industrial Uses

1) High doses of <u>gamma rays</u> will kill <u>all</u> living cells.
2) So gamma rays can be used to treat <u>cancers</u>.
3) Radioactive materials that give out gamma radiation can also be used as <u>tracers</u>.
4) Gamma rays are also used to <u>sterilise</u> medical instruments by <u>killing</u> all the <u>microbes</u>.
5) Gamma radiation can be used to do <u>non-destructive testing</u>.
   For example, <u>airlines</u> can check the blades of their <u>jet engines</u> by using gamma rays. If too much radiation <u>gets through</u> the blade they know the blade's <u>cracked</u>.

<u>Non-destructive</u> testing means testing something <u>without</u> <u>taking it apart</u> or <u>damaging</u> it.

Thickness gauges — they're called 'exams' nowadays...

Nuclear radiation can be <u>dangerous</u> and really <u>useful</u>. Make sure you know what <u>each type</u> is useful for.

The Solar System and the Universe

You're about to learn everything you need to know about the Solar System. Well, everything apart from whether there really are aliens out there. Learn this stuff first, then you can think about that later.

Planets Orbit the Sun

1) The Solar System consists of a <u>star</u> (<u>the Sun</u>) and lots of stuff <u>orbiting</u> (going around) it.

- The <u>planets</u> orbit the <u>Sun</u>.

- <u>Moons</u> orbit some <u>planets</u>.

- <u>The Moon</u> orbits the <u>Earth</u>.

- The <u>asteroid belt</u> orbits the <u>Sun</u> (see p. 116).

2) You need to learn the <u>order</u> of the planets:

Mercury,	Venus,	Earth,	Mars,	(Asteroids),	Jupiter,	Saturn,	Uranus,	Neptune
(Mad	Vampires	Eat	Mangoes	And	Jump	Straight	Up	Noses)

<u>Nearest</u> the Sun ⟶ <u>Furthest</u> from the Sun

3) Stars are <u>huge</u>, very <u>hot</u> and very <u>far away</u> — apart from the Sun, which is quite <u>close</u> to Earth.

4) They <u>give out</u> lots of <u>light</u> — which is why you can see them, even though they're so <u>far away</u>.

5) Stars can be <u>different sizes</u> but they all start life as a big <u>cloud of gas</u>.

6) Eventually they run out of fuel to burn and <u>die</u>.

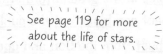
See page 119 for more about the life of stars.

There's More in the Universe than Just Stars and Planets

The Universe contains <u>all these things</u> that you need to know about:

1) <u>Stars</u>.

2) <u>Planets</u>.

3) <u>Comets</u> — balls of <u>rock</u> and <u>ice</u> that orbit the Sun (see next page).

4) <u>Meteors</u> — small chunks of <u>rock</u> that orbit the Sun close to the Earth.

5) <u>Galaxies</u> — <u>huge groups</u> of stars.

6) <u>Black holes</u> — what's left over when some stars <u>explode</u> (see. p 119).

The Solar System is Held Together by Gravity

1) Gravity pulls <u>everything</u> in the Universe towards <u>everything else</u>.

2) It's <u>gravity</u> that makes <u>planets</u> orbit stars, <u>moons</u> orbit planets and <u>satellites</u> orbit the Earth.

3) The gravity of a <u>black hole</u> is so <u>huge</u> that not even <u>light</u> can escape from it — this is why it's <u>black</u>.

Pull yourself together — get this stuff learnt...

Your brain doesn't just pull facts into it, so you're just going to have to get this stuff in there by doing some good, solid <u>revision</u>. Not the most fun thing to be doing, but better than being sucked into a <u>black hole</u>.

Asteroids and Comets

There's <u>more</u> than planets out there in the Solar System — aliens, space probes, but mostly just other <u>rocks</u>.

There's a Belt of Asteroids Orbiting Between Mars and Jupiter

1) When the Solar System was forming, the <u>rocks</u> between Mars and Jupiter <u>didn't form a planet</u>.

2) This left millions of <u>asteroids</u> — <u>bits of rubble and rock</u>.

3) They orbit the Sun between <u>Jupiter</u> and <u>Mars</u>.

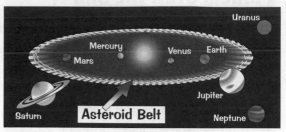

Not to scale.

Asteroids Have Crashed Down to Earth in the Past

1) Very <u>rarely</u> large asteroids <u>hit Earth</u>.

2) This can cause <u>problems</u>:
   - They can start <u>fires</u>.
   - They <u>eject</u> (throw out) loads of <u>hot rocks</u> and <u>dust</u> into the air.
   - They also make big <u>holes</u> in the ground (<u>craters</u>).

3) The <u>dust</u> from a large impact can <u>block out</u> the <u>sunlight</u>.

4) So the Earth will get <u>less heat</u> from the Sun and <u>cool down</u>, which can cause <u>climate change</u>.

5) Climate change can cause <u>species</u> to become <u>extinct</u>.

6) We <u>can tell</u> that asteroids have collided with Earth in the past because there's <u>evidence</u> for it:
   - <u>Big craters</u>.
   - Layers of <u>unusual elements</u> in rocks — these must have been <u>imported</u> (brought to Earth) by an asteroid.
   - <u>Sudden changes</u> in <u>fossil numbers</u> between different layers of rock — if lots of species become extinct at the same time then there will be fossils of the extinct species in <u>one layer</u> of rock and <u>no fossils</u> of them in the <u>next layer</u>.

Unusual elements are elements that <u>aren't normally found</u> on Earth.

Comets Orbit the Sun in Very Elliptical Orbits

1) <u>Comets</u> are balls of <u>dust</u> and <u>ice</u>.

2) They orbit the Sun in very <u>elongated</u> <u>ellipses</u> (squashed circles).

3) Comets <u>come</u> from objects orbiting the Sun <u>far beyond</u> the planets.

4) Heat from the Sun <u>melts</u> the comet's ice, leaving a bright <u>tail</u> of debris.

5) This tail is what we <u>see</u> from the Earth.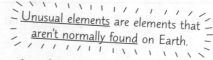

6) Comets <u>speed up</u> as they get <u>nearer</u> to stars (like the Sun).

Comet in an elliptical orbit (red line).

Asteroids hitting the Earth — I'm not going to comet on that...

Asteroids are a bit dull, really. Comets are much more exciting — it's the pretty <u>tail</u> and the weird <u>orbit</u>.

NEOs and the Moon

There are loads of lumps of rock just <u>whizzing about</u> in space — one of them might be coming <u>straight at you</u>.

Near-Earth Objects (NEOs) Could Collide with Earth

1) <u>Near-Earth objects</u> (NEOs) are <u>asteroids</u> or <u>comets</u> which might be on a <u>collision course</u> with Earth.

2) Astronomers use <u>powerful telescopes</u> and satellites to search for and <u>monitor</u> (keep an eye on) NEOs.

3) When they find one, they can work out the object's <u>trajectory</u> (the <u>path</u> it's going to take).

4) They use this to find out if it's going to <u>collide</u> with <u>us</u>.

5) NEOs can be difficult to spot because they're <u>small</u>, <u>dark</u> and may have <u>unusual orbits</u>.

~ If something's on a <u>collision course</u> it ~
~ means it's going to <u>hit</u> something. ~

Even Bruce Willis gets
it wrong sometimes.

The Moon May Have Come from a Colliding Planet

1) Scientists think that the Earth's Moon was formed when <u>another planet</u> <u>collided</u> with the Earth.

2) Billions of years ago a <u>smaller</u> planet <u>crashed into the Earth</u>.

3) In the heat of the collision, the <u>iron cores</u> of the two planets <u>merged</u> to form the <u>Earth</u>'s core.

4) The <u>less dense</u> material was <u>ejected</u> as really hot dust and rocks.

5) This dust and rock came together to form the <u>Moon</u>.

~ <u>Iron core</u> — the <u>centre</u> of ~
~ the Earth is made from <u>iron</u>. ~

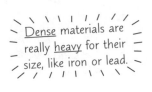

~ <u>Dense</u> materials are ~
~ really <u>heavy</u> for their ~
~ size, like iron or lead. ~

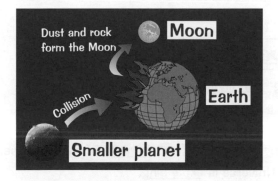

Dust and rock
form the Moon

Moon

Earth

Collision

Smaller planet

We Measure Distances in Space Using Light Years

1) Space is <u>really, really big</u> so we don't use normal measurements like kilometres to talk about distances in space.

2) We use <u>light years</u>.

3) One light year is the <u>distance light travels in one year</u>.

4) This is a <u>long way</u>. For example, the nearest star to the Sun is <u>40 000 000 000 000 km</u> away, but that's only <u>4.2 light years</u>.

Sadly the Moon isn't made of cheese...

Time for some exciting Moon facts — don't say I never treat you. There's <u>no evidence of mice</u> (or other life) on the Moon. Sad. When humans landed on the Moon they were worried that the surface wouldn't be <u>solid</u> enough and the landing craft would <u>sink</u> — not because they actually thought it was made of <u>cheese</u> though.

Understanding the Universe

To understand <u>space</u> and the Universe we need to <u>study</u> and <u>explore</u> it.

We Can Explore Space Using Manned Spacecraft

1) The Solar System is <u>big</u> — so big that even radio waves take <u>hours</u> to cross it.

2) This means it takes a <u>long time</u> to travel anywhere.

3) We can send <u>manned</u> spacecraft to explore space.

4) But the spacecraft would need to carry a lot of <u>food</u>, <u>water</u> and <u>oxygen</u>.

5) And it would be difficult keeping the astronauts <u>alive</u> and <u>healthy</u> for all that time.

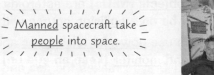
Manned spacecraft take people into space.

Space travel can be very stressful.

Unmanned Probes are Much Easier

1) <u>Unmanned probes</u> don't carry people but have loads of <u>instruments</u> instead.

2) The instruments are used to <u>record data</u> and <u>send it back</u> to Earth.

3) Probes (or people) sent to <u>places near Earth</u> could <u>bring back</u> samples.

4) Probes sent to really <u>far away</u> places have to <u>beam</u> information back using radio waves.

5) Unmanned probes can <u>collect</u> information about a lot of things:
   - <u>Temperature</u>.
   - Any <u>magnetic fields</u>.
   - How high <u>radiation levels</u> are.
   - How strong <u>gravity</u> is.
   - The <u>atmosphere</u> of a planet.
   - Its <u>surroundings</u> (if it lands on a planet, or moon, or asteroid).

6) Unmanned probes <u>don't</u> have to carry <u>food</u>, <u>water</u> and <u>oxygen</u>.

7) And they can cope with conditions that would be <u>lethal</u> (deadly) to humans.

Radiation levels are things like the level of microwaves or ultraviolet radiation the probe can detect.

The Universe Seems to be Expanding

1) The Universe seems to be getting <u>even bigger</u>.

2) It looks like <u>all the distant galaxies</u> are <u>moving away from us</u> very quickly.

3) <u>More distant</u> galaxies are moving away <u>faster</u> than nearer ones.

4) <u>Microwave</u> radiation is also coming towards us from <u>all parts</u> of the Universe.

5) The <u>conclusion</u> is that the whole Universe is <u>expanding</u>.

The <u>conclusion</u> is what the evidence suggests is happening.

This Evidence Suggests the Universe Started with a Bang

1) All the galaxies are <u>moving away</u> from each other really quickly.

2) Something must have <u>got them going</u> in the first place.

3) That 'something' was probably a <u>big explosion</u> — the <u>Big Bang</u>:

   1) Everything in the Universe was packed into <u>a very small space</u>.
   2) Then it <u>exploded</u>.
   3) The space started expanding, and the <u>expansion</u> is <u>still going on</u>.

In the beginning, there were — no exams...

'How it all began' is quite a tricky problem. Some religious people say that God created the world. The <u>evidence</u> suggests that the Big Bang is the <u>best explanation</u> for the start of the Universe — but maybe we'll never know.

The Life Cycle of Stars

Stars go through <u>many stages</u> in their lives but they do have a finite life.

<u>Finite</u> means it doesn't last forever.

Clouds of Dust and Gas

1) Stars <u>form</u> from <u>clouds</u> of <u>DUST AND GAS</u>.

Protostar

2) <u>Gravity</u> makes the gas and dust <u>come together</u> and the <u>temperature rise</u>.

Main Sequence Star

3) When the <u>temperature</u> gets <u>high enough</u>, a star is born. It enters a long <u>stable period</u> that usually lasts <u>several thousand million years</u>. During this stable period it's called a <u>main sequence star</u>.

4) Eventually the star <u>swells</u> into a <u>RED GIANT</u> (it becomes <u>red</u> because the surface <u>cools</u>).

Red Giant

Small stars

5) Smaller stars become unstable and <u>eject</u> their <u>outer layer</u> of dust and gas as a <u>planetary nebula</u>.

planetary nebula.... and a White Dwarf

6) This leaves behind a hot, dense solid core — a <u>WHITE DWARF</u>.

Big stars Red supergiant

7) <u>Big stars</u> start to <u>glow brightly again</u> as <u>RED SUPERGIANTS</u>.

Supernova

Neutron Star...

...or Black Hole

8) Eventually they'll <u>explode</u> in a <u>SUPERNOVA</u>.

9) The <u>exploding supernova</u> throws the <u>outer layers</u> of dust and gas into space, leaving a <u>very dense core</u> called a <u>NEUTRON STAR</u>.

10) If the star is <u>big enough</u> this will become a <u>BLACK HOLE</u>.

Red Giants, White Dwarfs, Black Holes, Green Ghosts...
Our Sun is going to fizzle out, and it'll get <u>very very cold</u> and <u>very very dark</u>. Great. On a brighter note, the Sun's got a good few years in it yet, so it's still worth passing those exams.

Galileo and Copernicus

Our models of the size and shape of the Solar System and the Universe have changed over time.

Ptolemaic Model — Earth at the Centre

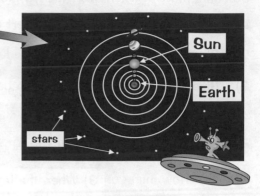

1) The Ptolemaic model says that the Sun, Moon, planets and stars all orbit the Earth in perfect circles.

2) The Ptolemaic model is also a geocentric model — it has the Earth at the centre.

3) It was the accepted model (the one people believed) until the 1500s, when it began to be replaced (see below).

A model is a bit like a theory — it's an idea that explains something.

Copernican Model — Sun at the Centre

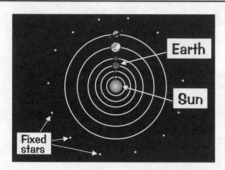

1) The Copernican model was introduced by Copernicus in 1543.

2) It says that the Earth and planets all orbit the Sun in circles.

3) And that the centre of the Universe is the Sun.

4) The Copernican model showed astronomy could be explained without having the Earth at the centre of the Universe.

5) The Copernican model is also a heliocentric model — it's got the Sun at the centre.

Galileo Found Evidence for the Copernican Model

1) Galileo was one of the first astronomers to use a telescope.

2) He used his telescope to find evidence to support the Copernican model.

3) Galileo saw moons orbiting Jupiter.

4) This showed not everything was in orbit around the Earth — so the Ptolemaic model was wrong.

5) Models and theories often change because of technological advances (like telescopes).

6) Galileo also noticed that Venus has phases (like the Moon).

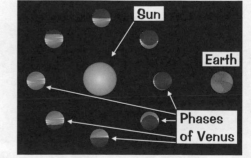

7) The amount of Venus that's lit by the Sun seems to change.

8) If the Ptolemaic model was right then the changes would be small.

9) But if the Copernican model was right, the changes would be big.

10) Galileo saw big changes, so it was more evidence for the Copernican model.

11) The current model says that the planets orbit the Sun but not in perfect circles, and that the Sun is not at the centre of the universe.

Copernicus — not a brand of metal underwear...

It's taken thousands of years and lots of new technology for us to reach our current model of the Solar System. All the models played a really important part in helping us reach the model we have today.

Revision Summary for Module P2

Just what you were waiting for — a whole list of lovely questions to try. Try the questions, then look back and see what you got right and what you got wrong. If you got any wrong, you're not ready for the exam. Do some more revision and then try the questions again.

1) Explain how wind turbines convert energy from the Sun into electricity.

2) Give one advantage and one disadvantage of using photocells to generate electricity.

3) Give three types of fuel that can be used in power stations.

4) Briefly describe how a generator works.

5) Explain why a very high electrical voltage is used to send electricity around the National Grid.

6) *a) How many units of electricity (in kWh) would a lightbulb of power 60 W use in 10 hours?

   *b) How much would that cost, if 1 kWh of electricity costs 12p?

   Units of energy = power × time

7) Give three examples of greenhouse gases.

8) Give the three reasons why carbon dioxide levels are rising.

9) Give one human and one natural cause for changes to the weather.

10) Name the three types of nuclear radiation.

11) Describe the precautions you should take when handling radioactive sources.

12) Which types of nuclear radiation are used in each of the following:

    a) medical tracers,   b) treating cancer,   c) smoke detectors.

13) Where are asteroids found in the Solar System?

14) What collided with the Earth to form the Moon?

15) Briefly describe the problems with sending a group of astronauts to another planet.

16) Briefly describe the 'Big Bang' theory for the origin of the Universe.

17) What will a small star become near the end of its life?

18) Describe the Copernican model of the Solar System.

19) Explain the evidence that Galileo found that supported the Copernican model.

Index

Index

Index and Answers

Answers

Wave Basics (page 59)

Speed = Frequency × Wavelength
= 2500 Hz × 0.2 m
= 500 m/s

Revision Summary for Module P1 (page 70)

2) Energy = Mass × SHC × Temp change
= 0.05 kg × 5000 J/kg°C × 40 °C
= 10 000 J

4) Energy = Mass × SLH
= 0.5 kg × 2 260 000 J/kg
= 1 130 000 J

8) Useful Energy = Total Energy − Wasted
Energy
= 200 000 J − 180 000
= 20 000 J

  Efficiency = Useful ÷ Total (× 100%)
= 20 000 ÷ 200 000 (× 100)
= 0.1 × 100 = 10%

11) Speed = Frequency × Wavelength
= 3000 Hz × 4 m
= 12 000 m/s

Power (page 110)

1) Power = Voltage × Current = 230 V × 12 A
= 2760 W
Divide by 1000 to get answer in kW:
2760 ÷ 1000 = 2.76 kW

2) Need to change minutes to hours:
3 mins ÷ 60 mins = 0.05 h
Energy = Power × Time = 2.76 kW × 0.05 h
= 0.138 kWh

Revision Summary for Module P2 (page 121)

6) a) 60 W ÷ 1000 = 0.06 kW
Energy = Power × Time = 0.06 kW × 10 h
= 0.6 kWh

  b) Cost = number of kWh × price per kWh
= 12 × 0.6 = 7.2 p